The Hierarchical Nature of
Personal Illness

The Hierarchical Nature of Personal Illness

G. A. FOULDS

MRC Unit for Epidemiological Studies in Psychiatry
University Department of Psychiatry
Royal Edinburgh Hospital, Edinburgh

1976

ACADEMIC PRESS

London   New York   San Francisco

A Subsidiary of Harcourt Brace Jovanovich, Publishers

ACADEMIC PRESS INC. (LONDON) LTD.
24/28 Oval Road,
London NW1

United States Edition published by
ACADEMIC PRESS INC.
111 Fifth Avenue
New York, New York 10003

Library of Congress Catalog Card Number: 76-1078
ISBN: 0-12-263250-8

PRINTED AND BOUND IN ENGLAND BY
HAZELL WATSON AND VINEY LTD
AYLESBURY, BUCKS

Preface

This book, like my previous one of ten years ago, is much concerned with the classification of the symptoms and signs of personal illness reported by psychiatric patients. This was not then, and probably is not now, regarded by many psychiatrists and by the majority of clinical psychologists as the most scintillating of topics. My persistence in pursuing it indicates my continuing conviction that all the other apparently more exciting activities would benefit from being conducted within a more logical classificatory system. I am thankful that I am not alone in this conviction. The past decade has seen the emergence of more rigorous attacks on the problem on both sides of the Atlantic.

Much of the evidence presented here for the hierarchical nature of personal illness has already appeared in various scientific journals, usually in collaboration with colleagues, especially Mr. Alan Bedford. Initial reactions to the hierarchy notion, even by psychiatrists with sound research to their credit, have frequently ended with "but, of course, I don't agree with you". One purpose in bringing the work together in one publication is to try to induce these critics either to demonstrate that faulty methodology has led to faulty conclusions or to furnish conflicting evidence. Otherwise even the most amicable disagreement has little heuristic value.

Although I have felt it necessary to criticize what I believe to be the over-extension of the theories of George Kelly and Carl Rogers, they have both made important contributions to the area in which my interests lie. My principal debt, however, is still to Professor John Macmurray's "The Self as Agent" and "Persons in Relation", which seem to me to provide much the most adequate underpinning for this type of work and to set the limits of psychological expertise.

I wish to express my gratitude to the many colleagues outside the M.R.C. Unit who have contributed much of the data. In Canada, where I began the work when a Visiting Professor at the University of

Western Ontario, I was greatly assisted by Dr. Kallman Csapo, Dr. Brian O'Neill and Mrs. Dorothy Weber. In England, Mr. Paul Pearson and Mr. Brian Sheffield supplied most of our normal sample as well as many psychiatric subjects. In Scotland, more psychiatric cases were provided through the help of Mr. David McIver, Dr. Frank McPherson and Dr. Allan Presly. In addition, I am grateful to Mr. Ralph McGuire for statistical and computer programming advice. So many psychiatrists and clinical psychologists have contributed ratings that I can only thank them collectively.

Much of my own pilot work was made possible through the co-operation of Professor Henry Walton of the Department of Psychiatry of the University of Edinburgh, the Department of Psychology and the University Hospital at the University of Western Ontario, Goderich Psychiatric Hospital and the London (Ontario) Psychiatric Hospital.

Within the M.R.C. Unit, a congenial atmosphere in which to carry out the work has always been created by the Director, Dr. Norman Kreitman, and I am grateful to him and to Miss Dorothy Buglass and Dr. Jack Ingham for valuable discussions. Mrs. Brenda MacSween has assisted greatly in many aspects of the preparation of the book.

Finally, I wish to thank my closest collaborator, Mr. Alan Bedford, who has held the project together and not lost the papers.

December, 1975

G. A. FOULDS
Medical Research Council Unit
    for Epidemiological Studies in Psychiatry,
University Department of Psychiatry,
Royal Edinburgh Hospital,
Edinburgh, EH10 5HF.

Acknowledgements

We would like to thank the following publishers for permission to quote from the books mentioned:

Academic Press, London—"The Evaluation of Personal Constructs" by D. Bannister and J. M. M. Mair.

George Allen and Unwin Ltd., Hemel Hempstead—"Dementia Praecox" by E. Bleuler.

Annual Reviews Inc., Palo Alto—"Classification of the behaviour disorders" by J. Zubin in *Annual Review of Psychology* (1967).

Baillière Tindall, London—"Clinical Psychiatry" by E. Slater and M. Roth.

Faber and Faber, Ltd., London—"Persons in Relation" by J. Macmurray.

Holt, Rinehart and Winston Inc., New York—"Assessment of Human Motives" Ed. G. Lindzey and "Principles of Behaviour Modification" by A. Bandura.

Houghton Mifflin Co., Boston—"Personality Development and Psychopathology" by N. Cameron.

Hutchinson Publishing Group Ltd., London—"Social Psychology and Individual Values" by D. W. Harding.

Jason Aronson Inc., New York—"How can the new diagnostic manual help?" by E. Gruenberg, *International Journal of Psychiatry*, **7**, 368–374.

New Science Publications, London—extract of book review by T. Szasz in *New Society*.

W. W. Norton and Co. Inc., New York and Messrs. Victor Gollancz Ltd., London—"The Quest for Identity" by A. Wheelis.

Oxford University Press, Oxford—"Textbook of Psychiatry" by D. K. Henderson and R. D. Gillespie; and "Three hundred years of Psychiatry" by R. Hunter and Ida MacAlpine.

Routledge and Kegan Paul Ltd., Henley on Thames—"The Causes and Cures of Neurosis" by H. J. Eysenck and S. Rachman.

Tavistock Publications, London—"Health and Sickness: the Choice of Treatment" by M. E. J. Wadsworth, W. J. H. Butterfield and R. Blaney and "A Dictionary of the Social Sciences" Eds. J. Gould and W. L. Kolb.

John Wiley and Sons Inc., New York—"Theories of Personality" by C. S. Hall and G. Lindzey; and "Personality Assessment" by W. Mischel.

together with the following professional bodies:

American Psychiatric Association, Washington, D.C.—"Depression: Disease, Reaction, or Posture?" (1968) by Sir Denis Hill, *American Journal of Psychiatry*, **125,** 445–457.
American Psychological Association, Washington, D.C.—"The Myth of Mental Illness" by T. Szasz (1960), *American Psychologist*, **15,** 113–118.

and the Editors of the following journals:
The British Journal of Medical Psychology—
"Hierarchies of personality deviance and personal illness" by G. A. Foulds and A. Bedford; "Validation of the Delusions-Symptoms-States Inventory" by A. Bedford and G. A. Foulds; "Has anybody here seen Kelly?" by G. A. Foulds and "Psychological construing in schizophrenics" by E. Williams and C. Quirke.
The British Journal of Psychiatry—
"Class change in the personal illness hierarchy" by G. A. Foulds, A. Bedford and K. Csapo; "The relationship between anxiety-depression and the neuroses" by G. A. Foulds and A. Bedford; "Psychiatric illnesses: some inferences from symptomatology" by A. E. Maxwell; "Eysenck Personality Inventory scores of patients with depressive illnesses" by R. E. Kendell and W. J. DiScipio; "Behaviour Therapy in complex neurotic states" by J. Wolpe; "Follow-up study of schizophrenia and depression in young adults" by J. A. Clark and B. L. Mallett; "The early symptoms of schizophrenia" by J. Chapman and "The psychiatrist in search of a science, III. The depth psychologies" by E. Slater.
The British Journal of Social and Clinical Psychology—
"A new personal disturbance scale (DSSI/sAD)" by A. Bedford, G. A. Foulds and B. F. Sheffield.
Psychological Medicine—
"Hierarchy of classes of personal illness" and "The classification of depressive illness: a re-evaluation" both by G. A. Foulds and A. Bedford; "Personality deviance and personal symptomatology" by G. A. Foulds and "A logical analysis of the medico-psychological concept of disease" by F. Kräupl Taylor.
The full details of all cited works are given in the References.

Contents

1

Personal Illness, the Specifically Human Illness

Introduction

Criticisms of the application of the medical model of illness to mental illness have been levelled at an outmoded version of that model. A more up-to-date version is necessary, but subordinate, to the personal illness model. This is the case because the organism is necessary, but subordinate, to the person and medicine's intrinsic concern is with the organism. Characteristics of the organism, in large part, we share with the animals. Characteristics of the person are probably specifically human. If they have application at all to any animals, it is certainly only to a very rudimentary degree.

When we become at least partially impaired in those functions which constitute us persons and when this impairment is sufficiently distressful to us, or to others acting on our behalf, that means are sought to restore our person-hood, we may be said to be personally ill. For these reasons illness of the person is considered to be the specifically human illness. Experimental "neuroses" do not provide an exact paradigm. The rat, we may presume, fears only what will be done to it, not what it will do.

There seem to be only two classes of individuals who are necessarily out of relation with other persons—those who are usually called mentally ill (who will generally be referred to here as personally ill) and those usually known as personality disorders. It is, therefore, to these two classes that attention will principally be given.

At a time when some psychiatrists and perhaps most clinical psychologists are rejecting the concept of mental illness, to seek to produce further differentiations within an illness model may seem like painting the lifeboats when the ship is sinking. It is necessary, therefore, to justify the retention of the illness model, albeit in a radically modified form.

Criticisms of the medical model

Those who have discarded the concept of mental illness argue that it should not be subsumed under the medical model because the analogy between physical and mental illness is misleading. Then, because the analogy is considered misleading, they wish to eliminate the concept of mental illness, or at least the term.

> One gets the impression that it is not the concept itself that is tabooed but only some of the words by which it is labelled, such as "disease", "sickness", "illness", "ailment", and the like. Other words, such as "special ab-normality" or "disorder" escape the taboo. (Kraüpl Taylor, 1971.)

The medical model has been described by Hornstra (1962) among others.

> The remarkable achievements of medicine had been based on the concep-tion of disease as a state of affairs or a process which had a specific aetio-logy, a predictable course, manifestations describable in signs and symp-toms, and a predictable outcome modifiable by certain describable manoeuvres. Mental illness became described according to the same basic notions.

That these remarkable achievements did lead to some crystallization of approach and a desire to extend that approach to untried areas was understandable in the Victorian hey-day when people still believed in Progress. Today this concept of the medical model is akin to grand-father's axe. It has had several new handles and several new blades since it was first constructed.

Critics neglect the fact that the medical model could and did quite easily abandon unicausation without disaster. No one now supposes that alcoholism is the *sole* cause of cirrhosis of the liver, cigarettes of lung cancer, excessive cholesterol of coronary thrombosis, or senile plaques of senile dementia.

Multiple causation, including both endogenous and exogenous factors, has long since been accepted; yet Milton and Wahler (1969) have written that

> while present advocates of the "medical model" tend to advance non-organic causes for behaviour deviations, the locus of their postulates is

still the same—*inside* the person. This sort of emphasis seems to confuse students.

Some may feel that, if this last criterion were widely applied, progress would indeed be slow.

The ignoring of so many new handles and blades suggests that a great need exists to believe that the sole cause of behaviour deviations lies outside the person. This need may have sprung, in part, from a social concern with shortcomings in current practice; but a more potent reason lies in the current, particularly American, *zeitgeist* that all evil lies outside the organism, outside the person. The Great American Myth used to be that anyone, if he worked hard enough, could become a millionaire and/or President. If he failed to do so, it was because he was a wicked lay-about. Since the success rate has proved disappointing, lack of success is now attributed to the System. It is Society which is evil or which promotes maladjustment.

The most wicked agents of Society are Parents. Responsibility for what used to be called "mental illness" rests largely with them. So cunningly and forcefully have Society and Parents conspired against the innocent Child that he has had no alternative but to accept the patient role.

This view has acquired enormous popularity. Placing responsibility for something undesirable upon someone else's shoulders has never been a policy which lacked adherents. This policy becomes especially attractive when the chosen scapegoats are Parents, since there will always be those who have failed to resolve their ambivalent attitudes to them.

The policy has the logical weakness that an infinite regress is implied. Failure to notice this suggests that the theory is an adolescent one. If one may be permitted to use a counter-exaggeration in this welter of exaggerations, adolescents believe that the world began when they were born. This ahistorical viewpoint overlooks the inconvenient fact that parents have habitually shown a propensity for once having been children. If the child be in no way responsible for his "mental illness", but has had it thrust upon him by his parents, the parents when they were children had their behaviour thrust upon them by their parents who, when they were children. . . .

One of the most influential of the opponents of the medical model has been Szasz (1960), who argues that mental illness has been hypostatized and then treated as the cause of disharmony between people, and that the analogy between physical and mental illness is seriously misleading. The first point is almost certainly factually incorrect in that it describes a view which is held, if at all, almost exclusively by members of the lay public. The second assertion is based on the outmoded idea of the medical model to which reference has already been made.

Szsaz says:

> Mental illness as a deformity of the personality—so to speak—is then regarded as the *cause* of the human disharmony. It is implicit in this view that social intercourse between people is regarded as something *inherently harmonious*, its disturbance being due solely to the presence of "mental illness" in many people. This is obviously fallacious reasoning, for it makes the abstraction of "mental illness" into a *cause*, even though the abstraction was created in the first place to serve only as a shorthand expression for certain types of human behaviour.

There may conceivably be a few psychiatrists and clinical psychologists who regard mental illness as an entity which is a sufficient cause of interpersonal disharmony; but it is very doubtful whether there are any who suppose that it is a necessary cause of interpersonal friction. If no one holds these opinions in fact and the notion is retained that mental illness is shorthand for certain types of human behaviour, the longhand translation would be that "certain types of human behaviour cause interpersonal disharmony", which seems unexceptionable and it is *not* implicit that social intercourse is regarded as "inherently harmonious".

Szasz believes it to be a widely held and erroneous opinion that the absence of mental illness "automatically insures the making of right and safe choices in one's conduct of life." He is thus attributing to others the belief: "Whenever mental health then right choices". Are there really any among us who believe that? Or is Szasz once again confusing necessary and sufficient conditions? There could conceivably be some who believe: "Whenever right choices then mental health"; but it is very doubtful whether any sophisticated expert in this field would really believe either that *all* of a mentally healthy person's choices were right or that *all* of a mentally ill person's choices were wrong.

Having convinced himself that mental illness has been treated as a causal entity, Szasz feels justified in speaking of The Myth of Mental Illness and states that his aim "is to suggest that the phenomena now called mental illness be looked at afresh and more simply, that they be regarded as the expressions of man's struggle with the problem of *how* he should live."

Presumably Szasz would agree that there are expressions of man's struggle which could not be subsumed under the category of phenomena now called mental illness. Either all expressions of man's struggle, from the schizophrenic smearing the wall with his faeces to Michelangelo smearing the ceiling of the Sistine Chapel, are to be treated alike or Szasz is under an obligation to supply differentiae, an obligation which he has not yet met.

Many of those who continue to conceptualize mental illness as falling within the medical model have changed their ideas of mental illness in accordance with changes in the medical model. This process has indeed been going on rather longer than Milton and Wahler (1969) seem to imagine. They believe that "it was probably about 150 years ago that psychotic behaviour . . . was first thought of as a disease." This is an error of almost two thousand years. Aulus Cornelius Celsus appears to have introduced the concept of "insanity" into the medical literature during the lifetime of Jesus (Bromberg, 1954).

It is perhaps salutary to remember that the one lengthy period during which the medical model was almost completely abandoned was The Dark Ages. Yet it is to The Dark Ages that Szasz frequently reverts for his attack on the concept of mental illness and the medical model. He deplores the concept of mental illness because it is a misleading analogy with physical illness, because it has been hypostatized and because it "is a true heir to religious myth in general, and to belief in witchcraft in particular. . . ." He goes on: "Our adversaries are not demons, witches, fate, or mental illness. We have no enemy whom we can fight, exorcise or dispel by 'cure'. What we do have are problems in living." Since we all have problems in living and since no clear differentiae have been spelt out, either we all require professional intervention or none of us does. It seems no more likely that Szasz's unwillingness to discriminate between the modern concept of mental illness and demonology will persuade those who adhere to the medical model to abandon it than it will arouse in them a nostalgia for The Dark Ages.

For his assertion that the analogy between mental and physical illness is seriously misleading Szasz found the support, among many others, of Adams (1964). He states that "the concept of functional mental illness is a verbal analogy" and went on to make it plain that he regarded it as a poor one at that. Szasz argues that physical symptoms can be distinguished from mental symptoms in being objective, ascertainable without personal involvement of the observer, and independent of cultural norms and ethical standards.

A brief selection of the points raised by Ausubel (1961) should suffice to demonstrate that he has dealt effectively with Szasz's first two criteria. Pain, as he says, is probably the most important and commonly used criterion of physical illness and nothing could be much more subjective than that. As to his involvement, the physician frequently has to decide whether a subjective report of precordial pain and tightness in the chest are symptoms of cardiac insufficiency, fear of cardiac disease and impending death, or both. As to Szasz's third point, epileptic seizures have been regarded both as signs of divine inspiration and of devil-possession. And yet in many quarters it is the views of Szasz, not of Ausubel, which prevail.

An outdated concept of physical illness and the medical model have been set up as a straw man, to which mental illness has been considered to be but poorly analogous. In consequence the illness notion has been discarded from mental illness. Szasz and like-minded psychiatrists and clinical psychologists have probably been eager to throw off Epiphenomenalism—the theory that mental events and processes are by-products of physical processes—but have failed to free themselves from philosophical dualism. Szasz, for example, has substituted for the old mind/body dualism a body/problems-in-living dualism. Furthermore, it is evident that physical illness is regarded as *the* model to which mental illness does or does not conform. Why should this be so? What gives physical illness this priority? The words "ill" and "disease" have denoted moral and mental states for at least as long as physical states. It will be argued that personal illness is the specifically human illness and that organic illness, which we share with the animals, is analogous to it. In both there are syndromes, patterns of presenting symptoms and signs, multiple aetiologies, sometimes a choice of treatments for particular syndromes and sometimes treatments applied to several syndromes.

According to Macmurray (1961), "the concept of 'a person' is inclusive of the concept of 'an organism', as the concept of 'an organism' is inclusive of that of 'a material body'." The concept of an organism is derived from the concept of a person by excluding from attention those characteristics which belong to the person category alone. Similarly, the concept of a material body can be derived from the concept of an organism by excluding from attention those characteristics which belong to the organism category alone.

Thus, all persons are organisms, but not all organisms are persons. All organisms (which includes all persons) are material bodies, but not all material bodies are organisms.

The term "organic" presents some difficulty as it has been used in more than once sense. When applied to personal behaviour, Macmurray claims, "it does not refer to that which we have in common with the animals, though it includes whatever of this there may be. It refers to the habitual aspect of personal activity in abstraction from the intentionality to which it is normally subordinate." A man may intend to walk to the Post Office to post an urgent letter rather than to go fishing; but his walking skill and style will be habitual. Often, however, an organism is thought of as an organized system, consisting of dynamically connected parts constituted to share a common life. Such a system persons do have in common with the animals. If this system undergoes a change which renders it incapable of carrying out its functions in such a way as to maintain that system, we might refer to it as ill or diseased.

Since the concept of an organism was derived, when a human being is concerned, by excluding from attention those characteristics which pertain to the person category alone, there is a sense in which the organism is an abstraction and thus unreal. We might, therefore, in this sense, speak of The Myth of Physical, or Organic, Illness. This is only the case, however, when we are considering the organism as an abstraction from the person; but the organism is necessary to, and included within the person. Thus no events can occur to the organism which do not occur to the person, in so far as the person includes the organism. This is not, however, to say that any *illness* which occurs to the organism must of necessity occur to the person *qua* person, that is, in the sense of those unique characteristics which distinguish the person from the organism.

A man may suffer a ruptured appendix without this in any way affecting his capacity to relate to other persons, even though his attention may temporarily be withdrawn from them. This could reasonably be described as illness of the organism. If, on the other hand, the man reacted with an acute anxiety state which generalized to all aspects of his physical health, his personal relationships might well be impaired by this constant preoccupation. He would then be classifiable as personally ill. Similarly, a prolonged anxiety state, which might impair personal relationships, may contribute to the development of a gastric ulcer.

Finally, a person with (say) obsessional symptoms will probably have an accompanying state of anxiety or of depression; but there is unlikely to be a concomitant change in the organism, other than that associated with the state of anxiety or of depression. In other words, interactions between organism and person are most likely to involve, on the personal side, states rather than symptoms. The distinction between symptoms and states will be elaborated in Chapter 4.

The least emphatic statement that one can make about the relationship between organism and person is that no one is likely to be organically better for being in poor personal health or personally better for being in poor organic health. A balanced view of this relationship, from the psychosocial standpoint, is presented by Mischel (1968) when he argues that

> A focus on the psychological conditions that govern disturbed behaviour, and on the rearrangement of psychological variables that can change them therapeutically, in no way preempts the role of physiological and genetic variables. The latter undoubtedly are absolutely critical in the genesis of behaviour, and ultimately may be harnessed effectively to achieve many changes in psychological problems. Moreover, there may well be limits on the kinds of changes that even the most potent psychological techniques can achieve—for example, in the re-education of brain-damaged patients. All that can be expected of an approach is that it concentrate on the variables with which it deals and that it try to go as far as possible with them.

It will be seen, in the following chapter, that these limitations have often been ignored

The personal illness and medical models

When we wish to think of a human being as a whole, as a unity, we must think of the person, since the person includes the organism; whereas the organism does not include the person. This concept of the person is not, therefore, an abstraction and is real. There can, therefore, be no meaningful sense in which one could speak of The Myth of Personal Illness.

Macmurray (1961) argues that the personal relation of persons is constitutive of personal existence. Two persons may be said to be in personal relationship when each is prepared to modify his original intention in such a way as to arrive at a mutually agreed intention and when the underlying motive of each is to sustain the integrity of the other. This is more than a compromise solution achieved as a result of bargaining. Some committee members may modify their intentions in order to come as close as possible to achieving their original intentions. The underlying motive only too often is fundamentally egocentric, to gain as much of one's own way as is feasible without regard for the integrity of the other. To the extent that one gains one's own way at this cost, one sets oneself apart from the other and diminishes oneself as a person. Even the most ruthless millionaire may, by donating large sums of money, seek to mitigate the damage done to the other, but, more particularly, to himself. Occasionally each member of a committee may consider the overall purposes of the committee so important that he is willing to accept an agreed solution, which may not correspond exactly with the original intention of any particular member. If the underlying motive be to sustain the common weal without damage to the integrity of any member, such members will find themselves entering into personal relations with each other.

If the personal relations of persons be constitutive of personal existence, then illness of the person must involve a change in one's relationship with other persons and some loss of the ability to intend one's own actions in a way which is usually consonant with the intentions of others. This change in relationship must comprise a change in attitude and accompanying affect. States of anxiety or of depression—with or without symptoms—are, as it were, an acknowledgement that this adverse change has got under way or is imminent.

In most normal relationships love and hate, trust and mistrust, sympathetic understanding and resentment co-exist. If the individual be sufficiently mature, sufficiently self-assured to sustain and avow these conflicting emotions, the positive attitudes, because they are—in the debased modern terminology—more rewarding, tend to become dominant. To the extent that each person is undefensive and, therefore, allocentric, each is likely to be more sensitive, to have a lowered threshold for perceiving cues, whether they be facial expressions, tones of voice or partially completed sentences. As with most ball games, skill in personal relations is probably hampered by too much deliberation and is enhanced at times when action seems to precede conscious thought. A basically loving relationship is seen as having its intermittent flaws.

If the individual be insufficiently mature, insufficiently self-assured, he has too hastily to resolve his conflict by disavowal. Under the intense

pressure of his hostile or fearful feelings he partially represses or scoto-
mizes his positive feelings and comes to regard the relationship as
essentially negative and only positive intermittently. Hostile feelings in
turn may give rise to guilt over harbouring such feelings against a
previously, or intermittently, loved one. Fearful feelings may result in
withdrawal from personal relations. Allocentricity gives way to egocentricity. The threshold for perceiving cues is heightened. The schizophrenic, by his extreme withdrawal, loses innumerable opportunities
for facilitating the process of inter-personal perception. If he responds
at all, he does so with deliberation over processes which should be
carried out preconsciously. Like the batsman at cricket who thinks too
much and is forced into playing a hurried defensive stroke, the schizophrenic misses the crucial moment. Repeated failure leads to still further
withdrawal.

In both the instances of hostile and of fearful feelings defences are set
up unconsciously against this intolerably distressful change in one's relationship both to the other and to oneself, the outward forms of which
are the familiar symptoms and signs of personal illness. Distress becomes
transferred to, and focused upon, the symptoms. Help is then sought
—either by the experiencing individual or by a close associate (often
the one implicated in the change)—to bring about removal of the
symptoms. Frequently this is the individual's conscious wish; but, because his defence dynamisms are operating below his level of awareness,
he is correspondingly unaware of the deeper distress he will have to
bear as his underlying attitudes and motives are exposed during the
course of the removal of his symptoms.

Little wonder that behaviour therapy, which seems to be capable of
removing a limited range of symptoms without evoking the deeper distress
associated with changed personal relationships, appeals to some therapists and to some patients. That it can markedly affect the individual's
ability to handle his personal relationships has not yet been demonstrated.

Symptom removal by any means is not, of course, to be despised.
Furthermore, it has not yet been established that a patient undergoing
a course of behaviour therapy necessarily learns nothing about that
essentially human aspect of human nature, his personal relation to
other persons. If he, in fact, does learn nothing of this, he may still be
in that much better condition for engaging in the task of improving
his personal relationships. It would, however, be surprising if the removal of symptoms by behaviour therapy improved his chances of

doing so alone and unaided. One would expect that there would be either a fairly immediate symptom-substitution or a recrudescence of something very like the original symptoms. Much of the evidence cited against these two possible eventualities is irrelevant. It is based on people who were not personally ill. If the individual be not personally ill, his quasi-symptoms may, indeed, merely be the result of faulty or unfortunate learning experiences. In such a case there would be no reason to expect either symptom-substitution or relapse to follow their removal. If, among the personally ill, symptoms be defences against the recognition of adverse and unacceptable changes in the person, mere removal of the symptoms without attention to the adverse changes in the person would be expected to lead either to symptom-substitution or to relapse. Such evidence as exists at the present time is inconclusive. The evidence will remain inconclusive unless behaviour therapists decide (a) to confine themselves to behaviour therapy, and (b) to behaviour therapy with people who are personally ill.

If relating be of the essence of person-hood, any failure to enter into or maintain mutual personal relationships would diminish the person *qua* person, and the individual would come that much closer—in the case of many chronic schizophrenics, very close indeed—to being nothing but an organism.

The personal illness model is seen, therefore, as inclusive of the medical model, which is derived by excluding from attention those characteristics which pertain to the personal illness model alone. The medical model is necessary, but subordinate, to the personal illness model.

The personal illness model is concerned with "the habitual aspect of personal activity in abstraction from the intentionality to which it is normally subordinate." It *is*, therefore, concerned with the organism in this sense; but the *aim* is to restore person-hood, that is to restore the ability to enter into mutual, personal relationships and the ability to intend one's own actions.

The medical model is essentially concerned with illness of the organism in the sense of "that which we have in common with the animals." The *aim* is to restore normal functioning of the organism. This is the aim of the medical model *per se*; but physicians and surgeons are increasingly aware of the fact that, for example, "successful" medical or surgical treatment of a gastric lesion does not ensure a "successful" outcome for the person. In consequence they are turning more and more to psychiatrists and to clinical psychologists for co-operation, because they acknowledge that medical men have no special expertise deriving from their discipline when it comes to illness of the person. This expertise may be acquired additionally by them in the process of becoming a psychiatrist; but there are no grounds, even then, for making the treatment of personal illness their exclusive province.

Medical training provides practitioners with certain skills and a sense of responsibility in dealing with sick people in general; but, at least until recently, it has put such practitioners at a disadvantage when dealing with illness of the person. To mention but one instance, the degree of detachment which facilitates the work of a surgeon would often hinder that of a psychiatrist. Some surgeons, by dissociating their attitude in the operating theatre from that at the bedside, have been very successful in overcoming these difficulties; on the other hand, some psychiatrists have never overcome the initial disadvantage of their medical training and have, in consequence, sought to apply the medical model as sufficient to the whole range of personal illness. It is this extreme position which has rightly come under heavy attack, especially from the social scientists. Unfortunately many social scientists are themselves often of equally inflexible orientation in denying the importance of forces within the organism throughout the entire range of personal illness—a theme which will be pursued in the next chapter.

The success of some physical treatments in psychiatry as palliatives is indubitable. Whether they are ever more than this, whether they are adjuvants to psychological treatment, depends upon their helping to create conditions in which the person can re-establish himself as the agent of his own actions. That this process of reorganization may occasionally appear to take place spontaneously is no excuse for leaving the patient at this critical juncture to his own devices. This trend has been in evidence for some years in many places. For example, during the last quarter of a century the time between the last electro-convulsive treatment and discharge seems steadily to have diminished. Even if the expectations of those psychiatrists who await the coming of the Biochemical Messiah for the cure of schizophrenia were to be met, this argument would still hold. Can one seriously envisage that very many individuals, who have for years been unable to enter into satisfying personal relationships, would suddenly and unaided be enabled to do so as a result solely of a change in their biochemical make-up? Lost skills may suddenly be recovered; unacquired skills cannot suddenly be acquired. To believe the latter would be to indulge in the magical thinking which Szasz (1960) rightly castigates. Total reliance on physical treatment is like providing a child with water-wings, but no instruction in swimming.

It is widely recognized that there are some symptom clusters which tend to recur frequently. Advocates of the disease-entity model attribute this to a specific underlying pathology. Many social scientists do not appear to realize that this was a minority opinion even when they began to launch their attack against it. Much more commonly clustering would be attributed to some, as yet dimly apprehended dynamic interaction between biological, social and psychological factors. Rejection of the disease-entity model enables one to allow for the possibility that symptom clusters may change their shape, as it were, and come closely to resemble some other well identified symptom cluster. It is worth noting in passing that this has important implications for studies of diagnostic reliability. Almost all such studies have been carried out within the disease-entity model, even by people who did not believe in it. Consequently a change in diagnosis over time has unquestioningly been regarded as evidence of unreliability of diagnosis rather than of a change in the stage of the illness.

If one acknowledge that symptom clusters may change and re-form at different stages of an illness, there is no good reason to expect that one type of treatment should be applied at all illness stages. Nor need one assume that the same person should necessarily apply that treatment. Different treatments at different stages of an illness, carried out by different people, are commonplace in medicine and surgery. Though by no means unknown in psychiatry, the full implications do not appear to have been thought through. Physical treatment may often be highly desirable in the acute stages of a psychotic illness and, if efficacious, may uncover neurotic symptoms, which should then be treated by psychological means. Of 36 patients diagnosed by the Symptom-Sign Inventory (Foulds and Hope, 1968) as psychotic depressives, 19 retained that diagnosis 4 to 6 weeks later. Nine had moved into the neurotic class and eight into the "normal" class (Foulds, 1965). The approach advocated here might conceivably reduce the distressingly high relapse rate.

It is probably not too fanciful to conceive of, say, a patient presenting with a severe psychotic depression being treated by electro-convulsive therapy, later by desensitization or flooding for phobias and, finally, by Rogerian non-directive counselling for the residual, more surface, anxiety or depressive state. It would be difficult to conceive of cases in which that treatment order might profitably be reversed. It is unlikely that any physical treatment alone should ever be the last treatment any patient received; it is equally unlikely that Rogerian therapy should ever be the first treatment any psychotic or severe neurotic patient received.

Although physical treatment is undoubtedly important in the treatment of personal illness, it is probably not necessary in every case and is probably never sufficient. Those psychiatrists and clinical psychologists who have been greatly influenced by sociology have often tended to deny the importance of physical treatment because they have regarded the causes of illness as being outside the organism or the person and have underestimated the extent to which the person creates his own environment. In consequence they have placed excessive emphasis on the failure of the individual to conform to certain cultural norms as the reason for people being classified as mentally ill. This negates the critical differentia between personality deviance and personal disturbance or illness.

It is true that perhaps the majority of the personally ill will deviate from certain cultural norms; but it is equally true that many, who are not considered to be personally ill, will do so. Until the relevant and critical norms have been specified and the extent of the deviation therefrom, this argument remains unconvincing. In essence, the personally ill deviate from their own norms; it is psychopaths who deviate from society's.

In the case of the personally ill what is of paramount importance is change within the person. It is the fact that the obscene thoughts of the ruminative obsessional are painfully at odds with the concept he had always had of himself, the fact that in these respects he is unable to intend his own thoughts and actions, which induces him to seek treatment —often after many years of acute distress which has never been conveyed to anyone. The psychiatrist does not label him (to use the popular pejorative term) as mentally ill because he believes that most people do not have obscene thoughts or because obscene thoughts are (or perhaps one should say "were") considered undesirable in our culture. The obsessional defines himself as in a state of, what Raven (1952) referred to as, "dis-ease" just as surely as if he had an acute physical pain.

Many paranoid patients complain to a doctor, not to the police, about the people who are trying to kill him. This seems to imply recognition of illness at some level of awareness. Why else would he take his "problem in living" (to use Szasz's phrase) to that source? The psychotic depressive—with a fine disregard for any mind/body dualism—protests that he is all rotten inside. Even severely disintegrated schizophrenics will complain that they are not right in the head. It is, of course, true that there are many psychotics who do not define themselves as sick. It is, however, a frequent occurrence that a relative, or other closely associated person, is aware of and concerned about the change within the person. It is this rather than the social deviance as such which prompts the seeking of treatment on the sufferer's behalf. The policeman who finds a woman wandering about the streets in her nightdress will not expect that his conduct will eventuate in the woman being sent to gaol, but rather to a mental hospital. She would be sent to a mental hospital not because she was in her nightdress and was, therefore, contravening a social norm, but because such behaviour—in the absence of evidence to the contrary, such as her house being on fire —would be regarded as indicative of mental derangement.

The extent to which concern is with change within the individual rather than with conformity to social norms might be said to be one of the hall-marks of a civilized society. Reported cases of individuals being incarcerated in mental hospitals in the Soviet Union because they have fallen foul of the regime reflect on the regime, not on the more usual professional concept of mental illness—Szasz (1971) notwithstanding. He believes that such occurrences are more frequent and more savage in America. This state of affairs he considers inevitable when psychiatrists are employed by the State. This may be an ingenious plea for even more private practice in America; but it reveals an ignorance of the fact that in Britain most psychiatrists are employed by the State and yet less than fifteen per cent of mental patients are involuntary, most of these for a very short time, and many safeguards for the patient are built into British Law.

Summary

Intervening, as opposed to innate, illness exists when there has been a change within the individual himself which results in some limitation or distortion of previous functioning and when this change occasions such distress or danger to the individual himself or, less often, to his associates or to society in general, that he seeks treatment or others seek treatment on his behalf.

If the change is initially and predominantly a change in the organism, the illness may be said to be a physical one; if the change is initially and predominantly a change in the person, the illness is a personal illness; if the change is initially organic, but results in a change in the person (as, say, in cerebral arteriosclerosis), the illness may be said to be a somatopsychic one; if the change is initially in the person, but results in a change in the organism, the illness may be said to be a psychosomatic one.

Personal illness is the specifically human illness. The personal illness model is inclusive of the medical model, which is important in the treatment of personal illness, but is neither sufficient nor necessary in every case.

The need has been emphasized to adapt the form of treatment in psychiatry to the various stages of an illness. This would entail the need to provide greatly increased facilities jointly for psychiatrists, clinical psychologists and for other associated workers under their supervision for training in various types of psychotherapy and of behaviour therapy. It would imply that one ought to be highly suspicious of any treatment which is claimed to be necessary and sufficient for the whole range of personal illness.

Acceptance of the view put forward of the relationship between the personal illness and medical models would entail some switching of attention from the place of psychiatry in medicine to the place of medicine in psychiatry. It is probably still largely true to say that a person enters a General Hospital and an organism is treated. This is probably rarely sufficient in a General Hospital and never in a Psychiatric Hospital.

2

Severity of Illness and Unconscious Motivation

Introduction

In Chapter 1 it was argued that illness of the person is the specifically human illness, because it involves at least a partial loss of that which constitutes us persons—that is, at least a partial loss of intentionality and of the ability to enter into mutual, personal relationships. These abilities are considered to lie outside the scope of the animals.

The personal illness model is concerned with "the habitual aspect of personal activity in abstraction from the intentionality to which it is normally subordinate." (Macmurray, 1961). It is, therefore, concerned with the organism in this sense; but the aim is to restore person-hood. The medical model, on the other hand, is essentially concerned with illness of the organism in the sense of "that which we have in common with the animals" (Macmurray, *op. cit.*) and the aim is to restore normal functioning of the organism.

Since the person is inclusive of the organism and since the organism is necessary, but subordinate, to the person, one must acknowledge that organic treatment may help to bring about conditions in which restoration of person-hood becomes more feasible. Extreme organicists, who have usually had in mind psychotic patients, have considered organic treatment to be sufficient and have tended to generalize about the whole range of personal illness from the severe end of that hierarchy. Though some of the most extreme organicists perhaps expect eventually to find a specific pathology in obsessional or hysterical neuroses, probably few would push this point of view as far as the so-called reactive depressives or free-floating anxiety states.

In this chapter it will be argued that the more severe the personal illness the more the patient's behaviour is determined by unconscious motives, the less he is able to determine his own future.

Like behaviour therapists, influential therapists and theoreticians, such as George Kelly and Carl Rogers, make little or no use of the concept of unconscious motivation and thus deprive themselves of perhaps the most important differentia among those who are personally ill, and between those who are personally ill and those who are not. It will be argued further that Kelly and Rogers may have been able to function successfully in psychotherapy without making inferences about unconscious processes because their clients were not as severely ill as those seen in more traditional psychiatric practice. Treating clients who have mild "problems in living", to reiterate Szasz's phrase, if preventative of more serious disorders, would clearly be a valuable activity; but it provides no sounder basis for generalizations about the whole gamut of personal illness than does the organicist's implicit exclusive reference to psychotics.

Severity of personal illness

The proposed hierarchy of classes of personal illness will be discussed in some detail in the next chapter. Suffice it here to say that it runs from dysthymic states (free-floating anxiety, elation and depression) through neuroses (phobic, obsessional and hysterical), integrated psychosis (paranoia, mania and/or depression) to non-integrated psychosis (the schizophrenics, including paranoid schizophrenia).

Severity of an illness is not determined by the number of symptoms or signs, nor is it determined by the intensity of distress experienced by the sufferer. It is determined by the extent to which the individual has ceased to be a person.

The paranoid patient with a single encapsulated delusion will be less readily understood by another person than will the monophobic patient or the hysteric with innumerable symptoms. He may be as competent as either of the neurotics in entering into impersonal relations with bus conductors, shopkeepers or bank clerks; but his ability to enter into mutual, personal relations will be more impaired.

The neurotic, in effect, is saying: "I cannot move my right arm; I have pains which move all around my body; I cannot go into very small, enclosed places; I have to count things again and again, even though I know it is ridiculous; but these disabilities are not me. They are alien to my true self." There is a hobbled self available for entering into, albeit, restricted and incompletely satisfying personal relations.

However encapsulated the delusional system of the paranoiac, it involves a gross distortion of his pre-psychotic concept of self. He believes that he is the rightful heir to the throne or that his wife is unfaithful. He is a much more important person than others think he is or than he thought he was before he became ill. Failure of others to accept his Kingship role constitutes a formidable barrier to his entering into mutual, personal relationships.

Severity of illness is not determined by the intensity of the distress experienced by the sufferer. That the agony of some obsessional compulsive neurotics may far exceed that of some elated manics or flattened schizophrenics will be readily accepted; but by the criteria suggested here, the neurotic is less severely ill. The neurotic knows that "there is some corner of a foreign land that is forever England", that there is a self to which the present symptoms are alien; the psychotic, particularly the schizophrenic, no matter how mild or few his symptoms, knows of no such corner and is much more unaware of his pre-psychotic self and much more alienated from other persons. The schizophrenic who believes that his thoughts, feelings and actions have been taken over by another clearly cannot intend his own actions. He does not know who he is or what actions, if any, are his own actions. He cannot, therefore, enter into mutual, personal relations.

Manic, paranoid and depressive psychotics construe themselves and others in ways for which there is no consensual validation. They do not choose to construe thus, but are driven to do so by motives outside their awareness. They do not intend their own actions and thoughts and, because others cannot apprehend their idiosyncratic construct system, they cannot enter into mutual, personal relations.

Hysterical, phobic and obsessional neurotics are aware of thoughts, feelings and actions which are not in accordance with their self-concepts. In these limited areas they are unable to choose how they will act, since they are driven by motives outside their awareness. Generalization from these limited areas does not seem to be such as to preclude all possibility of entering into mutual, personal relations.

While those who are relatively free from being driven by unconscious motives will be that much more able to intend their own actions, the possibility of achieving an intention may be limited by the physical world, by one's own constitution or by the intentions of others. Thus, a man may intend to run a four-minute mile; but his physique and the intentions of others in the race—in the form of their tactics—together with adverse weather conditions, may combine to frustrate the fulfilment of his intention and he may have to settle for a slower time.

Those who experience rather prolonged states of anxiety, elation or depression without neurotic or psychotic symptoms may be relatively well able to intend their own actions, but may be frustrated in the fulfilment of their intentions and, usually because of personality defects, be unable to adjust to these frustrations.

Underplaying the importance of unconscious defence dynamics and of unconscious motivation destroys the main ground for differentiating between the personally ill and the personally healthy and among the personally ill. The more severe the illness the less the individual is able to intend his own actions and thoughts, the more he is driven by motives outside his awareness, the less, therefore, he is able to choose, the more his behaviour is determined, the more he ceases to be a person, the more he becomes merely an organism. This view appears to be at odds with the opinion of many influential writers, such as Kelly and Rogers and the schools of behaviour therapy.

The theory and practice of non-directive counselling

Many therapists who virtually ignore the unconscious appear to be dealing with clients who are not seriously ill.

Hall and Lindzey (1957) have pointed out that

> the type of theory for which Rogers has shown a preference is one that fits the kind of data which have come out of a particular method of psycho-therapy . . . Rogers' view of the person has been shaped to a great extent by his therapeutic practices . . . Curiously, each of these theorists [Freud, Jung, Adler, Horney, Sullivan] arrived at quite different formulations on the basis of much the same sort of observations, namely, those provided by the verbal reports of patients in a therapeutic setting.

The main difference, which Hall and Lindzey go on to discuss, is that, while "the concept of unconscious motivation plays virtually no part in Rogers' thinking", the analysts felt the need to interpret the manifest content and believed that the latent content was unconscious and could be reached only by inference, never by direct observation.

This difference would not be curious if these analysts were treating much more severe cases than were, for example, Rogers and Kelly. One would expect the verbal reports to be quite dissimilar. It is hard to believe that the style of expression of a schizophrenic, of a ruminative obsessional and of an anxiety state would be very similar to each other and it would be a sad day if each were equally similar to that of the therapist.

Since Truax (1966) has shown that Rogers reinforces the patient's behaviour differentially according to the degree of similarity between the therapist's and the patient's style of expression, according to the degree of learning of discriminations, of insight and of problem orientation and, since this differential reinforcement is related to changes in patient behaviour over time-in-therapy, this would suggest that Rogers is likely to be more successful with some classes of illness than with others. In every instance the anxiety state would be more likely than the schizophrenic to give verbal reports which would receive differential reinforcement. If this were so, Rogers would be expected to be more successful in treating anxiety states than in treating schizophrenics and he would be wrong to assume that diagnostic knowledge is inessential as a pre-condition to psychotherapy, or certainly that it was useless.

It may be that the method of psychotherapy which Rogers has so skilfully developed took the form it did because it is appropriate for his particular clients, but that it may not prove appropriate for more seriously disturbed patients, at least in the early stages of their illness. Rogers (1957), however, believes that there are six conditions which are necessary and sufficient for bringing about constructive personality change in all cases, the most salient of which are that the therapist experience unconditional positive regard for the client much of the time and that he experience an empathic understanding of the client's internal frame of reference and endeavour to communicate this experience to the client.

If Rogers's clients be not severe cases, in the sense that they are relatively well able to intend their own thoughts and actions and are relatively little driven by motives outside their awareness, then one can readily understand that talking out their problems with an empathic and differentially reinforcing person will change their behaviour. This does not necessarily lead to a behaviouristic interpretation as Truax (1966) appears to assume. It may be that empathic warmth and differential reinforcement provide a cloth mother, a relatively anxiety-free context in which the patient can clarify his thoughts and attitudes.

If Rogers's clients be not severe cases, perhaps not—in the eyes of some—ill at all, he has little need to concern himself with the concept of unconscious motivation or of diagnosis as a pre-condition to therapy. Given such a sample, he may well come to believe that his six conditions are necessary and sufficient for bringing about constructive personality change. The danger comes when he generalizes from his sample to the whole range of personal illness.

It is not easy to grasp how a therapist can experience an empathic understanding of the internal frame of reference of a client who is incongruous in his affect, expresses himself in neologisms, word salads and knight's moves and believes that the thoughts in his head are not his own or, indeed, when he is in catatonic stupor. Whilst it is thought that this has been achieved to some degree by a few exceptional therapists at a great cost in time and personal equilibrium, it seems more realistic to conclude that there are many such patients with whom Roger's conditions can best be met after a course of physical treatment, though not always then.

Despite Rogers's (1961) claim that he has tried to be of help to "a broad sampling of our population", including normal, neurotic and psychotic individuals, there seems to be little evidence from his writings that he has spanned the entire range of personal illness. In what must be one of the most remarkable books ever to be produced in Psychology, Rogers and his collaborators (1967) provide, quite briefly, evidence which indicates that non-directive counselling was ineffective with a small group of schizophrenics. They then take up some six hundred pages teasing out the intricacies of the interpersonal processes which had proved ineffective. Notwithstanding the vast quantity and good quality of some of the research emanating from Rogers and his colleagues and followers and because of his attitude to diagnosis, one is left with a very unclear picture of the sorts of illnesses he has been treating.

Personal construct theory and practice

Reference has been made to differentiating between those who are and those who are not personally ill. There are those who claim that there is a continuum, that, therefore, the distinction is a very blurred one and is not worth the making. This kind of thinking is exemplified by Kelly

(1958) in his treatment of conscious and unconscious and of intellect and emotion.

> A construct owes no special allegiance to the intellect, as against will or the emotions. In fact, we do not find it either necessary or desirable to make that classical trichotomous division of mental life. After all, there is so much that is "emotional" in those behaviours commonly called "intellectual", and there is so much "intellectualized" contamination in typical "emotional" upheavals that the distinction becomes merely a burdensome nuisance.

Later he refers to cognition as a classical term that implies a natural cleavage between psychological processes, "a cleavage that confuses everything and clarifies nothing".

Only the most naive at this time would think in terms of a natural cleavage. The distinction between intellect and emotion is not generally considered to be like that between species. Nobody is reluctant to describe a person as tall or short, despite the known continuous distribution of height. Nobody would fail to acknowledge that there is more of intellect than of emotion in solving a crossword puzzle or an "intelligence" test; or that there was more of emotion than of intellect in making love. To deny this seems a trivial obfuscation.

While Rogers makes scant use of the concept of unconscious motivation, Kelly consciously wishes to have no truck at all with motivation, conscious or unconscious. He believes that the construct of motivation implies that Man is essentially inert.

> Examine what a person does when he is not being motivated. Does he turn into some kind of inert substance? If not—and he won't—should we not follow up our observation with a basic assumption that any person is motivated, motivated for no other reason than that he is alive?

No, we should not. It has long been recognized that the nervous system is always in a state of activity and that, as Peters (1958) has put it, explanation is needed of the patterning of activity rather than of its initiation. Furthermore, not all movement is either intentional or motivated, e.g. falling from an aeroplane, the Babinski reflex or any habitual activity such as the act of walking. It does not, therefore, follow that, because Man is never inert, the concept of motivation is redundant. It is required to differentiate at the very least between behaviour determined by fear of falling from an aeroplane and the happening of actually doing so. It is required to explain departures from the normal rule-following purposive model (Peters, 1958). Jack may have gone up the hill many times with Jill with the intention of fetching the pail of water. The climbing of the hill may have become quite habitual; but, on the particular occasion, Jack may have had a supplementary motive or intention. After all, we do not know how he came to fall down and break his crown and it is especially suspicious that Jill should have come tumbling after.

A man may intend to drown himself and do so, having left a note declaring his intention. We may know that he suffered from severe bouts of depression and we may guess that he was motivated by a desire to get out of this sinful world.

We may know that another man was in financial difficulties, that his wife had recently left him and that he went out to swim in a dangerously rough sea. We may have no evidence that he intended to kill himself; but we may guess that he was in a very disturbed state and was motivated to put himself into a Russian Roulette situation—not intending to die, but not intending not to die. He may even have made an unsuccessful attempt to save himself.

Yet another man—with no apparent cloud on his physical or psychological horizon—may have contracted severe cramp and been unable to save himself. We are aware of no intention or motive. Accidents do happen.

"For the psychotic", says Kelly, "with his pathways structured the way they are in his mind, he has simply chosen from a particular limited set of alternatives. How else can he behave? His other alternatives are even less acceptable." And "so long as he has some alternatives of his own making we must seek to explain why he chooses some of them in preference to others." And the Choice Corollary states that "a person chooses for himself that alternative in a dichotomised construct through which he anticipates the greater possibility for extension and definition of his system." Unfortunately Kelly then claims that "what we are saying in this crucial Choice Corollary gives us final ground for dismissing motivation as a necessary psychological construct." Further he states that "if we assume that his words and acts have less patent meanings . . . we must construe him in terms of a background understanding of his construct system." Bruner (1956) has done just that with Kelly, when he points out that

> an event is construed or "placed" at one or the other alternative poles of
> a construct . . . depending upon "which seems to provide the best basis for
> anticipating the ensuing events." One object of categorizing the world in

terms of a construct system is to minimize the disruptive surprises that it can wreak on us. This, I think, is the principal doctrine of "motivation" in the book—an implicit one, but one stamped on every page.

Kelly finds no need to distinguish between conscious and unconscious processes. "He organizes his constructs into a personal system that is no more conscious than it is unconscious." How we can know this if we do not make the distinction in the first place is as mysterious as knowing how we can examine someone when he is not being motivated when he is assumed to be motivated all the time. Yet "if they" (the personal constructs) "are important in a person's life, it is a mistake to say they are unconscious or that he is unaware of them." Is it permissible to say it if the personal constructs be unimportant?

This unwillingness to differentiate between conscious and unconscious processes leads him to make the curious statement that "To most therapists resistance is a kind of perverse stubbornness in the client. Most therapists are annoyed by it." The term "perverse stubbornness" is quite inappropriate for therapists whose constructs include the unconscious, with which resistance is usually associated. The claim that most therapists are annoyed by it seems patently absurd, since it is resistance which for them signals that they have made contact with a critical area. They would be more likely to be annoyed if they did not encounter resistance.

When the so-called resistance was finally broken through ... it seemed proper ... to ask ourselves and our client just what had happened. There were, of course, the usual kinds of reply, "I just couldn't say that to you then", or "I knew I was being evasive, but I just didn't know what to do about it", etc.

These may have been the usual kinds of reply from what Bruner (1956) called the post-adolescent peer groups of Columbus, Ohio, worried about their dates, their studies and conformity; but they would rarely issue from the mouths of the severe neurotic or psychotic patients in a mental hospital.

Mental hospital patients do differ from the usual run of University Clinic clients, particularly of America. One essential difference lies in the lesser availability to consciousness of the determinants of behaviour. Thus, a paranoid patient construed himself as half German and half Greek. When asked in what country he was born, he said "England". When asked in what country his father was born, he said "England". When asked in what country his mother was born, he said "England". When asked whether he had any reason to believe that any of his ancestors were born outside England, he said "No". When asked again what his nationality was, he said "Half German and half Greek". When asked what reason he had for thinking this, he was unable or (as Kelly would presumably have to say) unwilling to offer one. He was then asked, *inter alia*, if he could classify each of eight countries as either masculine or feminine. Germany was classified as the most masculine and Greece as feminine, though not the most feminine. Another of his constructs, or delusions, was that people were accusing him of being a homosexual. Of course he was aware of his Graeco-German construct and of his construct of people regarding him as a homosexual; but it seemed highly improbable that he was aware of any relationship between the two. Kelly would consider that to force such a patient to "utter words which do not parallel his constructs, or to mention events which are precariously construed, is to plunge him into a chaos of personal nonsense, however much it may clarify matters for the therapist." It seems unlikely that any skilled therapist would have forced this paranoid patient at that time to face up to the relationship between the Graeco-German and homosexual constructs which he, the therapist, might have believed to exist. It seems arguable that the patient was already plunged into chaos when he arrived in hospital. Why else did he come and why else was he willing to stay? But more important than that, is it really meaningful to say that this patient *chose* to be half German and half Greek?

This point comes out again when Kelly discusses the neurotic paradox, which Mowrer (1950) has described as "the paradox of behaviour which is at one and the same time self-perpetuating and self-defeating." Kelly concludes that, "from the standpoint of the psychology of personal constructs, however, there is no neurotic paradox." "The behaviour of the so-called neurotic client does not seem paradoxical to him until he tries to rationalize it in terms his therapist can understand ... within the client's limited construction system he may be faced with a dilemma but not with a paradox." One can only assume that Kelly's clients were, indeed, "so-called neurotics". No "real" neurotic would be likely to agree with him. If the compulsion to dress and re-dress twenty times in the morning, so that one is late, hours late, for work or for any appointment is not self-perpetuating and self-defeating, the terms have no meaning. Is our language so impoverished that we find it appropriate to say that such a compulsive patient *chooses* to dress and re-dress in this way? The man who believes himself to be devoutly religious, but finds that blasphemous thoughts keep coming into his mind against his will is faced with a paradox, not merely a dilemma. He is unconsciously motivated to blaspheme; but he does not intend to blaspheme. The extent to which psychiatric patients are unable to choose is an important differentia from normal persons.

Nowhere can the feeling that Kelly, like some behaviour therapists with their snake phobics, dealt mainly with clients who were not personally ill be better exemplified than in the statement that "we have talked about experiences with clients who, because they hoped we might be of help to them, honoured us with invitations to the rare intimacies of their personal lives . . ." Again, intimations of Columbus, Ohio! Neurotic patients are driven, usually very reluctantly, to seek help because their distress has become unbearable. It may be an honour for a therapist to be paid for minding other people's business; but it is not the patient's intention to confer that honour upon him.

If General Psychology has often placed disastrous reliance on university students, Psychopathology—or Psychopathology as understood by many clinical psychologists—is placing disastrous reliance on the clientele of university clinics. It would appear that many clinical psychologists are so strongly motivated to become involved in therapy, whether it be the non-directive, personal construct or behavioural brand, that they have been obliged to occupy themselves with—and have now acquired considerable proficiency in—curing people who have never been ill. This, if preventative, would be an activity of the highest importance; but it does not provide a sound basis for generalizations about the whole range of psychiatric illnesses. In view of the immense potential importance of this issue it is disappointing that so little effort has been made to determine whether treatment of the favoured kind prevents clients from becoming patients. If this be not done and if the therapist does not expose himself to the full range of the personally ill, he is, "bearing his blushing honours thick upon him", doubtless quite unwittingly and unintentionally trivializing the problem. Unless much greater caution and humility is exercised, this may well result in serious set-backs for the profession of Psychology in the future.

This dangerous situation arises from Kelly's brushing aside of diagnosis. To deny that diagnosis has any significance is implicitly to claim that the favoured form of treatment is equally efficacious with all patients. Kelly's philosophy renders it impossible for him not only to differentiate within the personally ill, but even to distinguish between people who are ill and people who are not.

For Kelly a construct has no existence independent of the person whose thinking it characterizes. There can be no question, therefore, of the truth or falsity of the construct, but only of its usefulness or convenience for the construer. The important problem, however, is whether or not the constructs have reference to anything outside the self. In the case of many psychotics they probably do not. Thus, a paraphrenic, who was visited in hospital, by his wife and a mutual male friend, construed the friend's tartan waistcoat as indicating that the friend was having an affair with the patient's wife. Presumably had they, in fact, been having an affair, the paraphrenic would have considered that his construct had been validated; but he did not need this evidence to satisfy himself. Every construct within the paraphrenic's delusional system is validated to his own satisfaction. There is no reference beyond the idea. This appears to hold for Kelly's theory in general.

Kelly, according to Bannister and Mair (1968),

> makes three assumptions about the universe—that it is real and not a figment of the imagination . . . in accepting that the universe contains real events and objects, Kelly also assumed that events internal to a person were equally real, so that thoughts or ideas about external things have a reality which is as convincing as the things themselves. Man comes to know something about the universe only in so far as he can make interpretations of it, and approaches an accurate awareness of events by successive approximations. The theory, then, is one which avoids the groundlessness and subjectivity of the purely phenomenological or existential approaches . . . Kelly accepts that . . . men . . . are distinguished by their capacity not merely to react to external events but to represent their environment . . . Man can only come to know the world by means of the constructions he places upon it and he will be bound by events to the extent that his ingenuity limits his possibilities for reconstruing these events. Each man erects for himself a representational model of the world which allows him to make sense out of it and which enables him to chart a course of behaviour in relation to it. Such a representation model or construct system, which may be explicitly formulated or implicitly acted out, may constitute a crude facsimile of many features of the world. However, a crude set of constructs is better than none at all, and as the world rolls along, constructions of reality may be tested out and modified to allow better predictions in the future.

If "man can only come to know the world by means of the constructions he places upon it", he cannot "react to external events", but only to his representation of these putative external events. He cannot be bound by events at all, but only by his representation of events. If he cannot react to events, he cannot predict them. He can only predict his own future representations of events.

If a man can know only his own representations of events, by what criteria can he judge that his modified successive approximations are more accurate representations of events which he cannot know?

What is meant by "implicitly acted out"? It must mean that some other person, whose existence cannot be proved, Y, infers from his representation of acts carried out by his representation of X that his (Y's) representation of X includes a particular representational model. Y can only reflect upon his own reflections. It is not adequate to make the gratuitous assumption that X and the universe are real, which presumably means exist independently of Y's thought about them. If we take Kelly's standpoint, X's existence must be proved by taking thought; but, as Macmurray (1961) has argued:

> The self conceived as spectator itself becomes a mere idea, since it is excluded from participation in what it contemplates. There is no place for it in the world. And whatever world its vision may be conceived to apprehend consists of its own ideas, as Descartes rightly recognized. It is more illuminating to recognize it frankly for what it is—a *reductio ad absurdum* of the theoretical standpoint. Existence cannot be proved; it is not a predicate. Yet the isolated self—the thinker—must prove existence if he is to apprehend the Other . . . We know existence by participating in existence. This participation is action.

So, within Kelly's Personal Construct Theory, to the question posed by the old music-hall song, "Has anybody here seen Kelly?", the answer must be "No", or, more accurately, there is nobody who can prove that he has.

If every construct within the paraphrenic's delusional system is validated to his own satisfaction because there is no reference beyond the idea and if this applies equally to Kelly's theory, this leaves him with no ground for distinguishing normality from abnormality, windmills from Don Quixote's construing of them. Little wonder that diagnosis is brushed aside. The normal person and the schizophrenic are equally withdrawn from reality, locked in an egocentric solipsistic construct system. Bannister uses consensual validation for determining the presence or absence of thought-process disorder in schizophrenics in his excellent studies of thought-process disorder in schizophrenia; but consensual validation is not a method which is open to the solipsist.

Summary

Rogers has claimed, and Kelly has implied, that the application of a single form of psychological treatment should be a necessary and sufficient condition for bringing about constructive personality change in all cases, including severe neuroses and psychoses.

Earlier personal illness was described as the specifically human illness and schizophrenia as its severest form. Psychiatry has been plagued throughout its history with bursts of unwarranted optimism. It should be stated and faced that there are still today individuals who never really recover from schizophrenia. Just as there has been a tendency to turn away from discussion and acceptance of physical death, so there has been a tendency to turn away from discussion and acceptance of this much more tragic psychological death. Innumerable theories and practices have sunk without trace in the shifting sands of schizophrenia.

The contribution which followers of Rogers and Kelly will be able to make to psychiatric treatment and to any theory of personal illness will be greatly reduced in scope, but one hopes enhanced in value, when modesty creeps in and the range of convenience is limited. Already behaviour therapists are showing encouraging signs of recovery from their earlier excesses and even seem prepared to abandon behaviourism in order to ensure some sort of survival.

Naturally diagnosis can be abandoned by therapists whose attentions are very largely confined to a clientele which is rather homogenous, self-selected and extremely remote from the severe end of the hierarchy of personal illness. Colleagues are entitled to know whether this be indeed the case. This knowledge can only come through diagnosis of some description.

3

Personality Deviance and Personal Symptomatology

Introduction

Since, in subsequent chapters, we will be presenting data based on the one hand on a symptom measure, and on the other hand a personality measure, this chapter will be concerned with the distinctions between them which constitute at least part of the framework within which we are operating.

Terms such as "traits" and "attitudes" are descriptive of attributes which sustain the normal continuity of the person; whereas symptoms, signs and states are disruptive of that continuity and indicate that the individual is personally disturbed and may be personally ill.

There is another class of individuals whose personal continuity is not disrupted, but who are nevertheless out of personal relation with others. These we will call the maladjusted personality deviants. The term is intended to imply that these are people who deviate extremely from the general run of the population on personality characteristics which appear likely to have a crucial and adverse bearing on the capacity to enter into mutual personal relationships.

There can be little doubt that individuals usually referred to as personality disorders or psychopaths constitute a major problem in most communities. They figure disproportionately in law courts, in prisons, in general and psychiatric hospitals, in special units for parasuicides, drug and alcohol addicts, the surgeries of General Practitioners and numerous other social agencies. In addition they wreak havoc in the lives of their associates. A vast amount of public money and professional time is expended on them largely to unknown, but almost certainly to unsatisfactory, effect. Comparatively, in these respects, schizophrenia is a minor problem; but the research time spent on schizophrenia seems far to exceed that spent on the personality disorders. Why should this be so?

As Harding (1953) has pointed out,

> if the individual's deviation seems to his companions to be due to constitutional inadequacies of equipment or to a disintegration or confusion of mind that makes his motives incomprehensible, they are then likely to judge him abnormal and thus to insulate themselves from him socially.

And again, "the deviant individual and his actions, once having been judged abnormal, are not socially disturbing and need not be taken seriously as a challenge to current standards and beliefs." One might add that, at least in the extreme case of schizophrenia, the manifestations are not disturbing to others in the sense that, in ordinary circumstances, most people never think, feel or act in a way remotely resembling the way in which a schizophrenic thinks, feels or acts. Absence of this threat to one's self-concept perhaps leaves one freer to feel compassion. In the case of the psychopath, with his extreme egocentricity and tendency to treat other people as objects, as instrumental to the often successful achievement of his goals, we feel no such immunity. We are only too well aware that this is something that most of us either do, or feel the urge to do, from time to time. Indeed, the psychopath frequently serves the function in our society of acting out our less reputable fantasies—hence the appeal of pornography and films such as "Butch Cassidy and the Sundance Kid", "Bonnie and Clyde" and "The Sting". Direct contact with psychopaths, however, brings few satisfactions. Probably only the exceptionally integrated or saintly person can feel compassion for someone who is blatantly trying to manipulate him. There is evidence (Walton et al., 1970) to indicate that the majority of psychiatrists do not claim to rise to such heights of forbearance, since they rather uniformly rated psychopaths as unlikeable. Indeed, the inability of the psychopath to enter into mutual personal relationships tends to force the psychiatrist himself into treating the psychopath as an object and thus the threat to his own self-concept is exacerbated and hostility mounts with every re-admission to hospital or wherever.

Both clinical and research work, in this area in particular, require a complex blending of empathy and detachment. The research worker can afford rather more detachment and so the personal barriers to the investigation of psychopathy are less and cannot alone account for the relative dearth of research in this area. Rather it would seem that methodological defects have led to or been consequent upon such conceptual confusion that investigators have been unable to find an appropriate framework within which to operate.

Five possible relationships between maladjustive personality deviance and personal symptomatology will be discussed and arguments advanced to suggest that only one of these relationships maximizes the chances of discovering the most appropriate framework within which to operate.

Before pursuing this issue further it is necessary to discuss traits and attitudes—since it is in certain of these that the maladjusted personality deviants are abnormal—and to put forward criteria for distinguishing between measures of normal and deviant attitudes and between both of these, on the one hand, and symptoms and states on the other.

Traits and attitudes

Whereas symptoms, signs and states of personal illness emphasize the discontinuities in behaviour and experience, those abstractions which we designate personality traits and attitudes emphasize the continuities.

Traits and attitudes can be distinguished from symptoms and states by means of at least four criteria. Unlike the latter, they appear to be normally distributed in the general population, to be universal, relatively enduring and usually relatively ego-syntonic.

Traits and attitudes, as assessed by people with a common frame of reference, are always universal in the sense that they apply to the total population under observation without exception. They are not universal, of course, in the sense that all cultures will utilize the particular concepts; but those who do use the concepts will be able to apply them to everyone. Thus, with the trait of motor speed, everyone—regardless of their culture—must fall within the range of very fast to very slow. The dimension can never be irrelevant to anyone. Similarly with the attitude of extrapunitiveness, the tendency to blame others when frustrated, everyone expresses this attitude in more or less degree and with more or less frequency.

The personality trait, or attitude, denotes a rather consistent position of an individual on some particular dimension. If all people manifested all forms of behaviour from completely controlled to completely uncontrolled affect in an apparently random way, the variable of affective expressivity might still be differentiable from other forms of behaviour; but the trait of expressivity in particular individuals would not be identifiable. Widespread inconsistency and specificity do not, however, seem to be the rule, so that the trait and attitude concepts have emerged as a means of classifying the relative generality, consistency and continuity of responses to somewhat similar situations. Many psychologists reject trait and attitude theory utterly, because they are disappointed in the relative lack of generality of responses. There is no disagreement over the fact that no one invariably behaves, say, extrapunitively or intropunitively in response to all types of frustration involving all types of individual. Some accept that the degree of generality that does exist can provide us with useful information, others do not.

In so far as consistency and continuity do occur, they probably tend to do so because, unlike symptoms, traits and attitudes are relatively ego-syntonic. We develop a particular trait, such as a characteristic style of walking, because it puts the least strain on our physical structure or musculature or because we think it graceful or impressive etc. A small boy may copy the walk of some football hero; but, provided it is reasonably consonant with his physique or he doesn't acquire a new hero, his style of walking will become habitual and the original reason for its initiation will be lost. We probably develop particular attitudes to the extent that we do from a vast variety of sources. We probably retain them because we believe them to be consonant with each other and with our concept of ourselves.

Newcomb (1950) considers that "a complete account of personality would have to show how characteristic patterns of expression are related to characteristic patterns of direction", where temperamental factors determine the manner of expression and attitudes determine the direction of the behaviour expressed. More specifically he says (Newcomb, 1964) that

> an attitude is the individual's organization of psychological processes, as inferred from his behaviour, with respect to some aspect of the world which he distinguishes from other aspects. It represents the residue of his previous experience with which he approaches any subsequent situation including that aspect and, together with the contemporary influences in such a situation, determines his behaviour in it. Attitudes are enduring in the sense that such residues are carried over to new situations, but they change in so far as new residues are acquired through experiences in new situations.

The inability of the psychopath to learn from experience is not considered to be a cognitive failing, but may well be an inability to acquire these new residues through experiences in new situations. He may be so strongly motivated to impress and to manipulate others to his own ends that every new situation is seen in the same light, so that in a sense he is not really open to new experience.

The term "trait" is being used to denote a characteristic style of acting. It is more constitutional, closer to the body, than an attitude, though it too may be a result of early learning at least in part. Thus, expansive-restricted gesturing, lability of affect, vocal characteristics and psychomotor speed are all regarded as traits; whereas extraversion-introversion, radical-conservative, and dominant-submissive are considered to be attitudes.

A trait, or attitude, may be *common*, or *normal*, if the position on a particular dimension is one which is shared by many other people; or it may be *uncommon*, or *deviant*, if it is rarely found in the same degree in the general population—say more than one and a half or two standard deviations above or below the normal mean. *Reference is to inter-individual variation*. This is why we stress that with psychopaths we are concerned with deviation from society's norms rather than from the individual's own norms.

Iago must have been at least a couple of standard deviations above the normal mean on hostility, which he manifested towards Othello, Desdemona, Cassio, Roderigo, his wife and, indeed, just about everyone with whom he came into contact. Every situation he encountered was an opportunity to manipulate others to his end of revenge on Othello. As he said of Othello, "I follow him to serve my turn upon him." He was, in short, a classical psychopath.

A personality trait, or attitude, may be *prominent*, or *salient*, if other traits or attitudes are not found in the same degree in the same person. *Reference is to intra-individual differences*. An individual may, for example, be extremely orderly, parsimonious and obstinate, but only moderately quick, intense in affect and hostile in his attitudes. His salient characteristics would, therefore, be orderliness, parsimoniousness and obstinacy.

Dickens used the method of concentrating on salient attitudes to the exclusion of common traits and attitudes with great effect in such characters as Mr Micawber—with his grandiloquently expressed optimism about his financial circumstances—and Uriah Heap—with his obsequiousness, which masked extreme hostility. To some extent we are probably all caricaturists of our acquaintances, if not of our friends. Clinical psychologists can only hope to be caricaturists of strangers and better caricaturists of acquaintances.

The uniqueness of any person in any particular sample of persons is a resultant in part of different strengths of traits and attitudes relative to other people and within himself. The different strengths of traits and attitudes, both between and within individuals, will have arisen as a result of the interaction between different constitutions and situations which the individuals did little or nothing to seek out, and between different constitutions and situations which already differing traits and attitudes have predisposed the individual to seek out in order to exercise them. Each individual may be unique in the eyes of God; but mundane observers can never hope to extend their observations to the entire population even of this world. Uniqueness cannot, therefore, be proved and, even if it could, it would be none of our business. Inevitably we seek to educe relations of similarity as well as of differences between people. Kelly (1955) made brilliant use of this fact in his repertory grid technique, when he asked subjects to say in what ways two people were alike and different from a third.

Perhaps many modern dramatists exaggerate our dismal failure to communicate with anyone. We know that there are some people with whom we can communicate much more readily and more deeply than with others, although we seldom know why. Kelly's claim that understanding of another increases *pari passu* with increasing similarity of personal construct systems may well have a substantial part to play, though not the only one.

Some people are much more alike than others, at least in their salient traits and attitudes, and this leads quite properly to the concept of types. This would be easily testable by Kelly's technique; but it is unlikely to be undertaken, since construct theorists do not like the idea of types. Though to an outside observer construct theorists seem much more alike than do other psychologists.

Edmund, in "King Lear", and Iago are much more alike than either is like Hamlet or Romeo. Hitler and Mussolini were much more alike than either was to Rembrandt or Fra Angelico. Some of the salient attributes of Rembrandt or Fra Angelico may have been deviant in that they may very rarely have been present in such extreme degree in the general population. It is clear from these examples that some deviant characteristics are much admired or, in the numerous less exalted examples which could be given, are socially acceptable; whereas others are considered socially reprehensible. The term "deviance" could serve to encompass all exceptional persons; but we need also a term which will differentiate within this class. Although earlier it was suggested that psychopaths deviate from society's norms and the personally ill from their own norms, it may be that psychologists should not be satisfied with social acceptability as a criterion, but should rather focus attention on the degree to which an individual's personality characteristics militate against his developing fully as a person, against developing mutual personal relationships. Slater's view seems to us unnecessarily pessimistic.

> The aim of thoroughgoing personality changes is not a therapeutic one in any normal sense, and what the change of personality is to be proves incapable of definition. It becomes impossible to determine the end-point at which the patient has achieved the required personality change and has become free to pursue the egoistic goal of personal self-realization. (Slater, 1975.)

We believe that some at least of the personality changes are capable of definition, that the patient will know when the end-point has been achieved and that he becomes free to pursue the alloistic goal of more satisfying personal relationships. Until we have more knowledge of what these criteria might be terms such as adjustive and maladjustive personality deviance, though themselves judgmental, might best serve.

Maladjusted personality deviants are then people who deviate markedly from the mean of the general population on attitudinal dimensions which are thought to have a crucial bearing on the capacity to enter into, or maintain, mutual personal relationships. Such dimensions may be legion. All one can hope to do initially is to investigate some of those dimensions which, in the light of decades of clinical experience and research, have been considered to have been of especial significance. Among the dimensions which have received much attention are hostility towards oneself and others, dominance-submission, dependency-independency, lack of empathy together with a tendency to manipulate others as objects. Each of these attributes, in their extreme form, may be considered to be facets of an egocentricity which renders vastly more difficult the maintenance of personal relationships.

The individual who continually acts towards others in a hostile, critical, domineering manner is seeking to destroy their possibility of choice and of intending their own actions, so that his own actions, choices and intentions may be given sole consideration. He, therefore, intends—or is motivated—to manipulate others in order to meet his own needs to the exclusion of theirs.

Someone who allows himself to be manipulated into behaving in a self-critical submissive and dependent manner is often equally egocentric. He is not seeking mutuality of experience, any resolution of problems by mutual consent. Rather he is saying, "I can only survive in these situations if I submit. Let others take the responsibility for decisions." In this way he diminishes himself as a person. It is easy to understand how the need to maintain dependency and irresponsibility may lead to the manipulation of others to that end even to the exclusion of the interests of the other.

The personally ill are egocentric in the sense that they are excessively self-absorbed; but the personally ill *per se* do not intend to manipulate others to their own ends. Some of those who are personally ill will in fact do so; but they will probably do so by virtue of being also maladjusted personality deviants. Hysterics, for example, are often thought of as manipulators; but this may be due to personality deviance being commoner among people suffering from hysteria than from many other forms of illness. Whether this is so remains to be seen; but the widespread belief that it is so may help to explain the equally widespread confusion between a diagnosis of hysteria and of hysterical personality.

If the self-absorption of the personally ill is consequent upon the development, or is an integral part, of the illness, one would predict that it would change with recovery from the illness. When the egocentric manipulation of others, whether it be predominantly extrapunitive or intropunitive, is habitual, when it outlives any personal illness, it is to be regarded as a deviant personality attitude.

Personality Deviance as a class will, therefore, be taken to contain all those who are at or beyond some agreed point towards either end of a trait or attitude dimension. The studies to be reported here are almost exclusively concerned with maladjustive personality deviance. Within this group a further differentiation is required according to whether or not such deviance has led to breakdown or to formal restraint. For the latter the term *personality disorder* will be applied.

Personal Symptomatology as a class will be taken to contain all those with recognised psychotic symptoms, neurotic symptoms or states, whether or not such symptoms or states have resulted in personal breakdown.

Guiding descriptions of the key attributes with which the studies are mainly concerned can be summarized thus:

A Sign is a qualitative change in bodily or mental functioning which is not reported as a distressful complaint, but which the skilled observer recognizes as indicative of such maladaptation as is likely to cause or to have caused danger or distress to others or to the patient himself. Most delusions are of this nature.

A Symptom is a qualitative change from a previous condition, such as is found very rarely in any random sample of the general population, about which the individual complains because it is distressing to him. For example, "I get in a complete panic in small, enclosed places."

A State is probably a quantitative affective change from a previous condition which endures at least for weeks rather than for days and where that changed condition is, though more frequently found than symptoms in any random sample of the general population, is nevertheless relatively rare. For example, "I sometimes go to bed not caring if I never wake up again."

An Attitude is a concept which serves to classify the relative generality, consistency and continuity of responses to somewhat similar situations. It is a more enduring condition than signs, symptoms or states and is usually normally distributed in the general population. If it changes at all, typically it does so only over an extended period of time. Sudden changes, such as religious conversions, are sufficiently exceptional to be worthy of remark. Some of these attitudes may frequently be found in extreme degree in certain abnormal groups such as parasuicides. These extreme attitudes may then be described as salient characteristics of that particular group.

Evidence about the distribution of signs, symptoms and states will be found in Chapter 7 and about the distribution of attitudes in Chapter 8.

Models for the relationship between personal symptomatology and maladjustive personality deviance

MODEL 1

The question appropriate for this model would be: "Does the subject fall within the Personal Symptomatology *or* the Personality Deviance class?"

This relation may be illustrated thus:

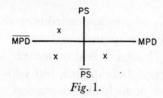

Fig. 1.

The Personal Symptomatology only (PS), the Maladjustive Person-
ality Deviance only (MPD) and neither ($\overline{PS}/\overline{MPD}$) quadrants are all
occupied; but the PS *and* MPD quadrant is void. This is to say that the
two classes are mutually exclusive, which alternatively be shown thus:

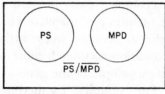

Fig. 2.

In this model, which is the one adopted by the American Psychiatric
Association and by the International Classification of Diseases, both
classes are regarded as falling within the same universe of discourse and
as being on the same level of classification. Each individual must be a
member of one of these classes only or of neither. In practice it often
happens that a clinician recognizes that the subject has some attributes
pertaining to each class; but, because he feels that he has to adhere to
the model, he allocates the subject only to that class which he regards
as the more important in the particular case. The criterion for "important" often remains obscure. Forcing clinicians to make decisions of
this nature almost certainly contributes disastrously to the unreliability
of psychiatric diagnosis.

The difficulties inherent in a classificatory scheme such as that of the
International Classification become most apparent when one considers
the groups within the Personality Disorder class and their relationship
to the groups within the classes of Neurosis and of Psychosis.

The relationship between a group in one class and a group in another
class ought to be the same as that between classes. In the International
Classification the relationship between the classes (e.g. Personality Disorder and Psychosis) is an either/or relationship. The relationship be-

tween a group within Personality Disorders and a group within Psychosis (e.g. schizoid personality and schizophrenia) should, therefore, be the same—either/or. To suggest that an individual must be categorized as either a schizoid personality or a schizophrenic is incompatible with the very widely held belief that schizophrenia is especially liable to develop in schizoid personalities and renders that belief untestable. In essential respects this is like asking "Is John an Englishman or is he tall?"

Since, in the International Classification, Personality Disorders, Sexual Deviants, Alcoholics, Drug Dependents, the Physically Disordered of presumably psychogenic origin, those with Special Symptoms not elsewhere classified and those with Transient Situational Disturbances are all given whole numbers from 301 to 307, they are all presumably intended to be classes on the same level of classification. One may, therefore, be placed in the unenviable position of having to decide whether or not a particular individual is an explosive personality disorder or a homosexual or an alcohol or a cocaine addict or a respiratory disorder or a stammerer or whether he is transiently disturbed.

It is no serious reflection on the diagnostic acumen of psychiatrists if they fail to achieve high inter-judge agreement in making such non-mutually exclusive discriminations. Early studies, which purported to demonstrate the low reliability of psychiatric diagnosis, took no cognizance of the impossibility of the task with which clinicians were being confronted. Later and better designed studies showed rather more satisfactory results; but even those bore little resemblance to what has recently been achieved by experienced clinicians operating within a more logical classificatory scheme (Wing et al., 1974).

The confusion which results from treating the classes of Personal Symptomatology and Maladjustive Personality Deviance as belonging within the same universe of discourse may be illustrated by three examples.

Foulds (1951) showed that the style of performance on Porteus Mazes of psychopaths (used in that study to include all personality disorders) was more like that of Hysterics than of Anxiety States, Neurotic Depressives or Obsessionals. One of the hazards of not differentiating between personality type and illness diagnosis has already been mentioned, namely that many hysteroid personalities are classified as Hysterics. Psychopaths have much more in common with hysteroid than with obsessoid personalities; obsessoid personalities, on the other hand, are relatively more common among the anxiety, depressive and obsessional groups. The results with the Mazes might, therefore, have been due more to personality than to diagnostic differences.

Marks (1965) compared the Semantic Differential of Obsessional neurotics and Psychopaths. A considerable number of his Psychopaths must have had neurotic symptoms. These symptoms would be least likely to be of an obsessional type. Psychopaths are more likely to be of hysteroid than of obsessoid personality and the opposite is true of Obsessional neurotics. One group would, therefore, be categorized predominantly as Obsessional neurotics of obsessoid personality and the other group as non-Obsessional neurotics of hysteroid personality. Marks would, therefore, be capitalizing on both diagnostic and personality differences without being in any position to weigh the relative importance of the contribution of each.

Eysenck (1960) combined a personality type (Psychopaths) with a diagnostic type (Hysterics) to form the criterion group for another personality type (extraverts). He also combined three diagnostic types (Anxiety States, Neurotic Depressives and Obsessionals) to form the criterion group for another personality type (introverts).

There is considerable evidence (Hare and Shaw, 1965; Foulds, 1968; Shepherd *et al.*, 1968) that at least those Psychopaths who are seen in psychiatric hospitals and, to a somewhat lesser extent, in prisons present the psychiatrist with abundant symptomatology—usually of an anxiety or depressive nature. Many of Eysenck's Psychopaths are likely, therefore, to have been Dsythymic States with psychopathic personalities. Should they, therefore, have been classified as Dysthymics and thus— according to Eysenck—as introverts; or, because they were Psychopaths, as extraverts?

More recently (Eysenck, 1968) has acknowledged that psychopaths and hysterical personalities would make better criterion groups for extraversion. Since, however, Anxiety States, Depressives and Obsessionals remain as the criterion groups for introversion, he is utilizing what would here be called deviant personalities as criterion groups for one end of his dimension and persons with particular types of symptomatology as criterion groups for the other end. At that point, therefore, Eysenck appeared to be accepting Model 4 (i.e. that Personal Symptomatology = Personality Disorder).

Further, Eysenck utilized psychopaths and neurotics together to validate a neuroticism dimension. In this respect he again implicitly conforms to Model 4; but, because he is accepting the either/or relationship between psychopathy and neurosis, he is also conforming to Model 1.

Model 1—the either/or relationship—suppresses one of the relata without having produced substantiating evidence for so doing. This model, therefore, discards potentially useful information and prevents further investigation of the relationship between maladjustive personality deviance and personal symptomatology. Since only a null hypothesis model can put Model 1 to the test, Model 1 should be abandoned until such time as this has been done.

MODEL 2

All those who fall within the Personal Symptomatology class fall within the Maladjustive Personality Deviance class; but *not all* those who fall within the Maladjustive Personality Deviance class fall within the Personal Symptomatology class.

In Model 2 the Personal Symptomatology *and* Maladjustive Personality Deviance (PS/MPD), the Maladjustive Personality Deviance only (MPD/$\overline{\text{PS}}$) and the neither ($\overline{\text{PS}}/\overline{\text{MPD}}$) quadrants are all occupied; but the Personal Symptomatology (PS/$\overline{\text{MPD}}$) only quadrant is void. This may be illustrated thus:

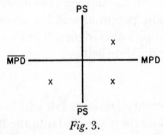

Fig. 3.

This is to say that PS is inclusive of MPD. All PS are MPD; but not all MPD are PS. Alternatively, this may be shown thus:

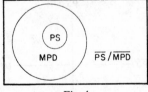

Fig. 4.

This was the model proposed earlier (Foulds, 1965), when it was claimed that all the personally ill are personality disorders, but not all

personality disorders are personally ill, and these are the psychopaths.
The attributes which were thought to distinguish personality disorders
(and, therefore, the personally ill in addition) were stated to be an extreme egocentricity, inability to empathize and a tendency to treat
other people as objects. The personally ill do often manifest the first two
criteria. The error arose in part through overlooking the likelihood that,
among the personally ill, these attributes may not have been present
before the illness and may be indicative of a change in the individual.
Blackburn (1972), for example, has shown a significantly lower extrapunitive score among "recovered" than among "ill" manics and extrapunitiveness is heavily implicated in measuring egocentricity, lack of
empathy and treating others as objects (Presly and Walton, 1973).
Among Maladjustive Personality Deviants, on the other hand, these
attributes are probably more or less life-long. Furthermore, Maladjusted
Personality Deviants can probably be differentiated from the personally
ill by their tendency to manipulate others for their own ends. The egocentricity of the personally ill is a self-absorption which often does not
permit of a sufficiently detailed or accurate construing of others to enable manipulation to take place (see, for example, McPherson *et al.*,
1971b in Chapter 5).

As in Model 1, once the assumption is made that all PS are MPD it
becomes untestable. The potential number of combined classes is restricted without any empirical evidence. This model should also, therefore, be abandoned for the time being.

MODEL 3

All Maladjusted Personality Deviants fall within the Personal Symptomatology class; but *not all* those who fall into the Personal Symptomatology class fall within the Maladjustive Personality Deviance class. This
can be illustrated thus:

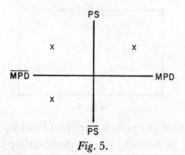

Fig. 5.

This is equivalent to saying that MPD is inclusive of PS, which, alternatively, may be shown thus:

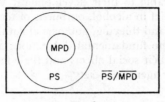

Fig. 6.

Although the widespread use of Model 1 may have obscured the fact that very many personality disorders seen in psychiatric hospitals are also personally ill at that particular time, there is no evidence to suggest that all are so and there is some evidence to suggest that all are not so.

The remaining criticisms of Model 2 apply equally to Model 3. This too should, therefore, be abandoned meantime.

MODEL 4

This model posits a relationship of identity or of degree. No distinction is made between personality traits or attitudes and symptoms, at least in kind and at least in the area of what are commonly called the neuroses and personality disorders. There is thus only one dimension and the relationship may be illustrated thus:

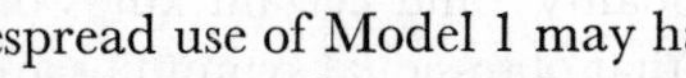

Normal   MPD   PS

Fig. 7.

or thus:

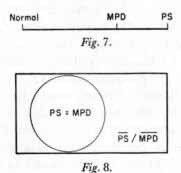

Fig. 8.

This view is held by, for example, Jaspers (1963) and Schneider (1958) and is implicit in a factorially derived classification system such as Eysenck's.

The view is clearly expressed by Slater and Roth (1969):

Tachycardia, sweating, feeling of fear, insomnia, depression, faints, fugues and the other phenomena which we call neurotic symptoms, are easily thought of as manifestations of a given personality and constitution in circumstances favourable to their development. We could also consider tendencies to seek relief in alcohol, outbursts of temper, wandering, dereliction of duty, lying and thieving, and acts of ruthless cruelty in the same light. There can be no fundamental distinction; and such distinction as there is depends on their social effects and their liability to be dealt with by doctors or by other agents of society

Slater and Roth's claim would be more tenable if the association between "a given personality" and certain kinds of symptoms was well established. It is true that obsessional symptoms are "easily thought of" as arising from an obsessional personality; but they can also arise in quite other types of personality. In these cases the association is not at all easy to understand.

"Neurotic symptoms may easily be thought of 'by an observer' as manifestations of a given personality and constitution in circumstances favourable to their development"; but, to the individual experiencing the symptoms, this is most commonly not the case. He feels that his symptoms are alien to his "real" self, that they constitute an inexplicable disruption of the normal continuity of his experience. This is much less likely to be so with "dereliction of duty, lying and thieving, and acts of ruthless cruelty". Deviant behaviour, however, such as excessive cruelty or excessive drinking, requires further analysis. The tendency to seek relief from depression in alcohol is very different from alcoholism resulting from a habitual inability to inhibit antisocial or self-destructive behaviour. An act of ruthless cruelty may be committed by someone during the course of a schizophrenic illness in response to voices. Such a person, when not ill, might never exhibit cruelty to anything like the same degree. This is basically different from someone who is habitually cruel and callous. The difference in duration of these phenomena is often quite apparent and should not be ignored. Furthermore, we will show, in the next chapter, that symptoms and personality characteristics are very differently distributed both in normal and in abnormal populations.

As with the first three models, the assumption in this model of a relationship—this time of identity—prevents further investigation of other possible relationships. Existing evidence does not seem to justify such a closure.

MODEL 5

Some who fall within the Personal Symptomatology class also fall within the Maladjusted Personality Deviance class and some do not; some who fall within the Maladjusted Personality Deviance class also fall within the Personal Symptomatology class and some do not.

Model 5 may, therefore, be illustrated thus:

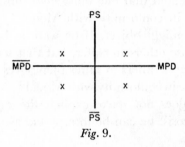

Fig. 9.

All four quadrants should be occupied. The relationship is an either *and/or* one, which alternatively may be shown thus:

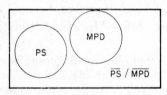

Fig. 10.

For Schneider (*op. cit.*), as for Szasz and many others, only those conditions for which there is evidence, or a reasonable presumption, of an organic basis fall within the medical model. On this ground Schneider would remove psychosis from the Personal Symptomatology class. We are left, therefore, with neurotics and personality disorders; but he believes that neurotics do not exist as a class. They constitute a group within the class of psychopathic personalities. This class is divided into two groups—those who suffer (the neurotics) and those who cause others to suffer (the sociopaths). The conceptual distinction is clear; but the relationship between the groups is not spelt out. As it stands, Schneider would appear to be accepting Model 1, the mutually exclusive relationship.

If Schneider were to hold that *all* those who suffer cause others to suffer, but that *not all* those who cause others to suffer themselves suffer, he would be in conformity with Model 2. If he were to hold that *all* those who cause others to suffer themselves suffer, but that *not all* those who suffer cause others to suffer, he would be in conformity with Model 3. In both these instances, however, the inclusive relationship would render impossible acceptance of sociopaths and neurotics as groups on the same level of classification within the class of psychopathic personalities. If he were to hold that one must *either* suffer *or* cause others to suffer, he would be in conformity with Model 1, however much the spouses of neurotics might object. If he were to believe that some of those who suffer cause others to suffer, but that some do not *and* that some of those who cause others to suffer themselves suffer, but some do not, then he would be in conformity with Model 5.

Since Schneider does not make explicit the relationship between sociopathy and neurosis, he can be interpreted as a possible supporter of Models 1, 2, 3 or 5.

There do appear to be grounds for distinguishing between psychopathology and personality characteristics and for accepting the fact that the evidence with regard to the relationship between them is far from conclusive. Model 5 has, therefore, been adopted in the studies to be reported for the reason offered by Zubin (1967):

> One major source of confusion in diagnostic work stems from the differences in points of view regarding the relationship between psychopathology and personality . . . At the present time, the evidence is equivocal with regard to the tenability of any one of these propositions . . . In view of this situation, the null hypothesis of no relationship may be adopted and double entry tables for the classification of patients along both dimensions may yield better classification.

We would argue, however, that a dimensional approach is usually inappropriate for the illness problem, though highly desirable for personality measurement.

It is crucial to the determination of which model is correct that we be able to measure symptoms, states, deviant and normal personality traits and attitudes. Some measures which appear to be useful within these classes will be discussed in Chapter 4. Meantime, since Personal Symptomatology and Maladjustive Personality Deviance have been referred to as classes independent of the notion of breakdown, it is necessary to consider groups within each of these classes who have and who have not broken down.

Coping and not coping

It was held (Foulds, 1965) that symptoms must be distressful either to the subject himself or to others, but that their presence did not constitute a sufficient condition for the diagnosis of personal illness and that some "breakdown" or "unmanageability" concept was needed in addition.

It has always been apparent that there are people in the community with distressing symptoms who cope with varying degrees of success. Some of these people have been studied by Mayo (1969) and his results indicated that women with high scores on the Personal Illness Scale of the Symptom-Sign Inventory (Foulds and Hope, 1968), who had not broken down scored as high on Hostility (Caine et al., 1967) as neurotics about to begin treatment. Both groups scored higher than low scorers on the Personal Illness Scale. The neurotics in treatment were, however, significantly more intropunitive than both the other two groups, when the intropunitive-extrapunitive difference was scored. People with high Personal illness scores who had not broken down tended to score relatively higher on extrapunitiveness. They also tended to disclose less to their "most significant other" person.

Consideration of these results suggested the possibility that Mayo might have been picking up a few personality deviants who were coping —at least in the sense of never having sought treatment or of not having been forced into treatment or prison. If extreme attitudes, which prevent an individual from entering into personal relationships or which are a consequence of his being unable to do so, are distressful either to the individual himself or to significant others, then distressfulness would appear to be the salient characteristic common to all classes within Personal Symptomatology and Maladjustive Personality Deviance. The universe of discourse which encompasses both of these classes could then be named "Personal Distress".

Figure 11 shows the universe of Personal Distress and the relationship between the classes of Personal Symptomatology and of Maladjustive Personality Deviance. Within the large circle on the left (Y) are those who have Personal Symptomatology. In the smaller circle (X) are the Personally Ill, completely contained within Y, whose symptoms are distressing either to the subject or to society and are unmanageable either by the subject or by society. All X are, therefore, Y; but not all Y are X—and these are the Personally Disturbed (y), whose distressing symptoms are manageable both by the subject and by society. This is Mayo's group and explains why the Personal Illness Scale was later changed to the Personal Disturbance Scale. This part of the universe is completed by those who are symptom-free $(\overline{Y})$, the Personally Healthy.

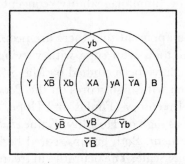

Y = Personal symptomatology   B = Maladjustive personality deviance
X = Personal illness   A = Personality disorder
y = Personal disturbance   b = Discordant personality
$\overline{Y}$ = Personal health $\overline{B}$ = Normal personality

Fig. 11. The universe of Personal Distress: Personal Symptomatology and Maladjustive Personality Deviance.

Within the large circle on the right (B) are all those whose traits or attitudes are distressing either to the subject himself or to society, the Maladjusted Personality Deviants. In the smaller circle (A) are the Personality Disorders, completely contained within B, whose distressing attitudes are unmanageable either by the subject or by society. All A are, therefore, B; but not all B are A—and these are the Discordant Personalities (b), whose distressing attitudes are manageable both by the subject and by society. This part of the universe is completed by those whose attitudes are not distressing either to the subject himself or to society $(\overline{B})$, the Normal Personalities.

The term "Maladjusted Personality Deviant" is being used, therefore, to contain all those whose traits or attitudes are distressing either to the subject or to society regardless of their manageability.

Although no one who is classified as personally ill can at the same time be classifiable as personally disturbed or as personally healthy, time, traumata or treatment may bring about moves in either direction between any classes. Many people leave hospital still personally disturbed. Sometimes the psychiatrist has to be content to enable the paranoid patient to live with or keep to himself his delusions of persecution. In such cases the symptoms or signs remain, but possibly there has been a sufficient reduction in the associated state of anxiety to make the symptoms more manageable. In the opposite direction, a personally healthy individual may lose his children in a car accident and react to his loss by developing a state of depression and move either into the personally disturbed or personally ill class, according to whether or not he manages to cope.

No one who is classified as a personality disorder can at the same time be classifiable as a discordant personality or as a normal personality; but time, traumata or treatment may effect moves in either direction, at least between the personality disorder and discordant personality classes. A head-injury might result in movement from the normal personality class to either of the other two; but this would, of course, be Karpman's (1941) symptomatic psychopathy. A discordant personality might get by in war-time but break down under the extreme rigours of peacetime existence. Movement to the normal personality class from either of the other two would be thought to be quite exceptional, although it is sometimes considered to occur with increasing age. Here, however, it is not known whether there is a change in the personality structure or whether the hitherto frequent adverse consequences of that personality structure have been curbed.

The same considerations of exclusiveness do not, of course, apply across the Personal Symptomatology and Maladjustive Personality Deviance classes. An individual can at one and the same time be deemed to fall within each, in accordance with Model 5. The circles in Figure 11 have, therefore, been shown as overlapping. Theoretically there are nine possible categories, all of which seem likely to be filled. These are:

1. Personally Ill personality disorder $(X:A)$—an aggressive hysteroid psychopath commits a crime and wanders off in a fugue.
2. Personally Ill discordant personality $(X:b)$—a man with a strong submissive-dependent need, whose wife has helped him to cope, develops a depressive state after her death.
3. Personally Ill normal personality $(X:\bar{B})$—a man of normal personality has a series of traumatic war experiences and develops an acute anxiety state.
4. Personally Disturbed personality disorder $(y:A)$—a man copes

with some phobic symptoms by avoidance, but is constantly in trouble for ill-treating his wife after drinking bouts.

5. Personally Disturbed discordant personality (y:b)—a man who copes with periods of depression—perhaps by heavy, but not addictive drinking—and whose irresponsibility and abnormal egocentricity are coped with by his wife.

6. Personally Disturbed normal personality(y:$\overline{B}$)—a man who bears with his obsessional ruminations and otherwise utilizes his compulsive meticulousness creatively.

7. Personally Healthy personality disorder ($\overline{Y}$:A)—a sadist with no symptoms who commits a murder, who might have belonged to the next class before doing so. This is the classical, but rarely seen, cold, callous psychopath unacquainted with guilt.

8. Personally Healthy discordant personality ($\overline{Y}$:b)—a man with no symptoms, who worries about his aggressiveness, but manages to sublimate it sufficiently to keep out of trouble.

9. Personally Healthy normal personality ($\overline{Y}$:$\overline{B}$)—a person who has no symptoms, whose traits and attitudes are reasonably congruent with his self-concept and the concept others have of him and who does not unduly alarm society. The reader will doubtless be able to supply at least one example for this class.

Summary

Five possible models of the relationship between personal symptomatology and maladjustive personality deviance have been discussed. The null hypothesis of no relationship is the most useful to adopt at the present time, since all the others assume a relationship for which there is as yet insufficient evidence. Only the null hypothesis model is capable of providing that evidence.

In the universe of discourse of personal symptomatology we are primarily concerned with deviations from the individual's own norms; in the universe of maladjustive personality deviance we are mainly concerned with the individual's deviation from general population norms. This deviation may be positive or negative in the sense of acceptable or unacceptable to society in general. Although negative, or maladjusted personality deviants constitute a far bigger social problem than do schizophrenics, there is vastly more research done on schizophrenics.

The even greater neglect of positive personality deviants, though under-standable, is nonetheless regrettable. This group and the group of those who have managed to cope with their symptomatology need much more investigation. It would be more likely to increase our understand-ing of personal illness and its treatment than is the study of chronic schizophrenics.

Epidemiological studies have reported incidences and prevalences of psychiatric illness or disturbance that have varied enormously, even ludicrously. One of the reasons for this has been the failure to agree about which of the classes discussed here should be included. Some investigators have included all except $\overline{Y}:\overline{B}$ (the personally healthy normal personalities). Not surprisingly they have uncovered little "normality".

If investigators go on to ignore the difference between needing and wanting treatment, they may spread confusion. Since the vast majority of cases likely to be in question will be non-psychotic, wanting may conceivably be the best guide to needing. There is as yet insufficient evidence concerning the quality of coping among those with symptoms who do not break down and seek treatment. Behind the zealous desire to spread psychiatry more widely lies the belief that all emotional dis-tress should be alleviated rather than worked through. Even where this belief did not exist originally, successful proselytizing would inevitably result in such an unfavourable psychiatrist-patient ratio that the damp-ing down of affect would become more and more mandatory. It is not enough to "cure" very minor conditions; it is necessary to demonstrate that such "cures" reduce the chances of a more severe illness developing later.

If a study does not provide separate figures for personal illness and personal disturbance and again for personality disorder and discordant personality, not only is the needing-wanting problem burked, but so also is the need for longitudinal investigations into the possible person-ality and social differences between distressed persons who do and who do not cope with their problems. The implication is that Mayo's investi-gation needs to be extended to include maladjustive personality devi-ance as well as measures of personal symptomatology. Ideally these measures should be applied to several thousand people in the general population, who should then be followed up for at least fifteen years in the hope that one might be able to determine what sorts of people in what sorts of situations are especially vulnerable or especially resistant to psychiatric and other forms of social breakdown. If one makes the assumption that those personality characteristics which remain constant during and after episodes of personal illness are likely to have been present in the same degree before breakdown, a more immediately practical alternative is available.

4

The Hierarchy of Classes
of Personal Illness

Introduction

In this chapter it is argued that important inclusive relationships have been relatively neglected in psychiatry and clinical psychology. They are implicit in the writings of some authors in respect of particular pairs of illnesses; but they have never been used explicitly through the whole range of functional psychotic and neurotic illnesses to build up a cohesive system of psychiatric classification.

An inclusive, non-reflexive, relationship exists where all the attributes of class B are contained within class A, but where some of the attributes of class A are not contained within class B. Thus, acting-out hostility is inclusive of the urge to act out hostility. Those who do act out their hostility must have an urge to do so. There are, on the other hand, people who have the urge to act out hostility, but do not in fact do so. It may be that neurotics and Henderson's (1947) inadequate psychopaths have the urge and don't; whereas his aggressive psychopaths have the urge and do.

If, as Makhlouff-Norris and Gwynne Jones (1971) state: "intra-self and social alienation are not independent in that the former inevitably implies some form of the latter, but the converse is not necessarily true", then intra-self alienation is inclusive of social alienation. All those who are self-alienated are socially alienated; but not all those who are socially alienated are self- alienated.

It has been suggested (Foulds, 1973; Foulds and Bedford, 1976) that protagonists in the debate about the status of neurotic and psychotic depression have posed an inappropriate either and/or question and have thus obscured an inclusive relationship. Evidence was presented that virtually all those with the symptoms of psychotic depression had the symptoms of neurotic depression, but that the converse did not hold.

As early as 1845 Ernst von Feuchtersleben wrote: "Every psychosis is, at the same time, a neurosis; because without the intervention of nervous action, no change of the psychical action becomes manifest, but every neurosis is not a psychosis, of which convulsions and pain afford sufficient examples." Certainly he was using the terms psychosis and neurosis differently from the current usage—rather more akin to person and organism as used here—but he was undoubtedly putting forward the notion of an inclusive, non-reflexive, relationship.

Wing *et al.* (1974) stated that "clinical diagnosis is hierarchical" without fully elaborating their belief. This has previously been done in more detail by Gruenberg (1969). APA classification, he said, "has a simple logical structure in which the manifestations of each condition can include the manifestations of the subsequent conditions, but the later conditions do not include the manifestations of the conditions listed earlier". He went on to say that "it could mean that the genius of the psychiatric profession has over the years discovered a latent logic inherent in mental disorders. But I am more inclined to think that we have simply imposed on the clinical phenomena which come to our attention a classification scheme in which we give logical priority to conditions with the most varied manifestations and recognize that some forms of mental disorder are less heterogeneous in their manifestations." This is in agreement with our initial statement of the problem (Foulds, 1964). "It may be helpful to think of a continuum . . . In terms of such a continuum, non-integrated psychosis implies psychosis and, therefore, personal illness, and psychosis implies personal illness. This is so logically and may possibly be so historically. This does not imply that all melancholics, for example, have obsessional symptoms. What it does imply is that melancholics have, with comparable frequency, all those symptoms which are equally common in all neurotic sub-groups."

Modifications to the original position were made some years later (Foulds, 1971) and further changes have followed. Most recently it has been proposed that it may be useful to consider that there are four classes of personal illness, each with its constituent groups, ordered by increasing degrees of adverse change in the person.

Class 1. Dysthymic States (DS). Groups: states of Anxiety (sA); states of Depression (sD); and states of Elation (sE).

All of these states refer to changes in affect (Foulds, 1971). An individual in any of these states might be said to be *disturbed*, emotionally stirred up, altered in this respect from his normal self.

Since this separation of dysthymic states from neuroses is unusual, an attempt will be made below to set out possible differentiae.

Class 2. Neurotic Symptoms (NS). Groups: Conversion symptoms (CVs); Dissociative symptoms (Ds); Phobic symptoms (Ps); Compulsive symptoms (CPs); Ruminative symptoms (Rs).

Here the subject may be said to be in a state of *dissonance*, in that he views a part of his behaviour and experience as alien to his normal self.

Class 3. Integrated Delusions (ID). Groups: delusions of Persecution (dP); delusions of Grandeur (dG); delusions of Contrition (dC).

This class refers to persons whose self-concept has become *distorted*, warped or otherwise grossly exaggerated.

Class 4. Delusions of Disintegration (DD). Groups: Those who in addition to suffering from delusions of disintegration, suffer from one or more of the integrated delusions. Paranoid, as opposed to non-paranoid schizophrenia, might, for example, be indicated by someone who fell into both DD and dP, as contrasted with someone who fell into DD but not dP.

The implication here is that the person has *disintegrated* to a very considerable extent as a person, in that he has lost his concept of himself as agent of his own actions, feelings and thoughts.

The prediction is that a person with symptoms at any class level will have symptoms at *all* the lower class levels and that a person without symptoms at any class level will not have symptoms at *any* higher class level. This is the inclusive nature of the relationship. The relationship is also non-reflexive in that only *some* of those persons with symptoms at a particular class level will have symptoms at the higher class levels.

Figure 12 illustrates the hierarchical arrangement of the classes of personal illness and shows the combination of classes for five individuals. Person 5 has symptoms at all four class levels and is, therefore, diagnosed as Class 4 (DD); Person 4 at the three lower ones and is, therefore, diagnosed as Class 3; Person 3 at the two lowest levels and is, therefore, Class 2; Person 2 at the lowest level and is, therefore, Class 1 and Person 1 is non-personally ill ($\overline{\text{PI}}$).

Although confining himself to the functional psychoses, one of the

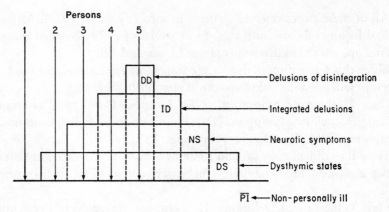

Fig. 12. A schematic diagram of the inclusive relationship of the hierarchy of classes of personal illness

earliest and most eminent psychiatrists to make rather explicit use of an inclusive, non-reflexive, relationship was Eugene Bleuler (1950). "All the phenomena of manic-depressive psychosis may also appear in our disease; the only decisive factor is the presence or absence of schizophrenic symptoms. Therefore, neither a state of manic exaltation nor a melancholic depression, nor the alteration of both states has any significance for the diagnosis. Only after careful observation has revealed no schizophrenic features may we conclude that we are dealing with manic-depressive psychosis."

True, Bleuler does not say that all schizophrenics are manic-depressives or, in our terms, manifest delusions of either grandeur or of contrition; but, if one adds delusions of persecution, the probability runs fairly high. At the least, Bleuler is saying that, when both conditions are present, schizophrenia takes precedence. This provides some justification for dividing the functional psychoses into the two classes of non-integrated and integrated delusions.

Chapman (1966), after a careful examination of the early symptoms of young schizophrenics, decided that

> taking the group as a whole, every kind of neurotic symptom was encountered in the early stages of the disease. This is, of course, in agreement with many other clinical studies . . . In particular, intense anxiety reactions were almost invariable, occurring more frequently than depression.

Again, Chapman does not say that all schizophrenics are neurotics, although he comes very close to saying that they are all dysthymic states. Furthermore, Chapman's interviews were directed towards eliciting and describing schizophrenic symptoms; whereas, neurotic symptoms were not the focus of specific enquiry. In spite of this limitation of enquiry, he does mention that at various stages of their illness some of these schizophrenics underwent "a transient period of mild elation", others, or the same ones at a later stage, "one of intense anxiety" and still later "short bouts of depression with suicidal ideation". If the depression was psychotic in nature, Chapman is virtually saying that at least some schizophrenics manifest the symptoms of each of our classes 3, 2 and 1.

Although it is not a necessary part of our hypothesis that patients move up the hierarchy, it must clearly be a subject of enquiry. One statement of Chapman's appears to deny such movement. "It is true that the schizophrenic psychosis may be masked by multiple neurotic symptoms, but there seems little doubt that schizophrenics experience the basic symptoms from the outset." But outset of what? If the basic symptoms define the illness, naturally they must be there at the outset of the schizophrenic illness; but, since neurotic symptoms were not the subject of specific enquiry, we are not to know that neurotic symptoms were absent before the onset of the schizophrenic illness. The issue must remain open until interviews have directed equal attention to the symptoms of all classes and groups of illnesses.

Gittleson (1966a) found that of 398 cases of depressive psychosis, 31% had obsessions during the course of their psychotic illness and 5% showed a transition from obsessions to delusions. He also noted (Gittleson, 1966b) that 13% had frank pre-morbid obsessional symptoms. Within a disease entity model, "pre-morbid" must mean before the onset of the depressive psychosis. Within the hierarchy model, one would say that 13% of subjects who subsequently developed a depressive psychosis previously suffered from an obsessional neurosis. Once again a hierarchical classification is implied. There is no question of the 31% who had obsessions during the course of their psychotic illness being classified as "Mixed obsessional neurotics and psychotic depressives"; and the hierarchy is clearly uni-directional. Few psychiatrists would think of classifying Gittleson's cases as "Obsessional neurosis with psychotic depressive features", Chapman's as "Anxiety states with schizophrenic features" or Bleuler's as "Manic-depressive psychosis with schizophrenic features", even if some would deny the hierarchy to the extent of describing them as "Schizo-affective psychosis".

Clark and Mallett (1963) carried out a three-year follow-up on 186 patients under the age of thirty.

> Approximately 70% of the schizophrenic group required admission to a mental hospital within the three-year period, and 93% of those admitted were again diagnosed schizophrenic. Of the depressive group, 20% required admission, of whom about two-thirds again had depressive illnesses and one-third were diagnosed schizophrenic.

Strictly in terms of a disease entity model, one or other of the diagnoses in this last group must have been "wrong"; in terms of the hierarchy model, one-third had moved up the hierarchy.

Berrington et al. (1956) found evidence of a prodromal state of depression in their fugue states, indicating movement in some cases at least up the hierarchy from class 1 to class 2.

Sheldon Roth (1970) wrote of the seemingly ubiquitous depressions, both neurotic and psychotic, following acute schizophrenic episodes and thought they needed treating as such. Here we have the suggestion of movement down the hierarchy from class 4 to either class 3 or class 1.

Jackson (1970), although seeming to dislike the idea of a psychotic-neurotic continuum, claimed that "some of the most severe neurotic symptoms are seen in psychotics of all types".

Finally, Maxwell (1973), summarizing his earlier paper (Maxwell, 1972), noted:

> In that study a representative sample of patients was considered under the three broad categories, neurotics, affective psychotics, and schizophrenics, and it was seen that all had a basic core of symptoms of the type generally referred to as "neurotic" . . . in addition the schizophrenics, and to some extent the affective psychotics showed symptoms of the type generally referred to as "psychotic" . . .

While it is of interest in passing to note that some affective psychotics did not have psychotic symptoms, Maxwell does appear to be saying that all psychotics are neurotics, but not all neurotics are psychotic. The suggested relationship is again inclusive and non-reflexive.

It seems safe to conclude from this brief review of the literature that some psychiatrists believe that some whom we have designated class 4 patients have symptoms pertaining to classes 3, 2 and 1; that some class 3 patients have symptoms pertaining to classes 2 and 1 and that some class 2 patients have symptoms pertaining to class 1. Our hypothesis substitutes *all* for *some*.

We must now try to justify the separation of Dysthymic States from Neurotic Symptoms.

Neurotic symptoms and dysthymic states

Both neurotic symptoms and dysthymic states are terms used to describe a change from a previous habitual condition. With symptoms the change is most probably qualitative; with states it is more likely to be quantitative.

Most people never suffer from a functionally paralysed limb; nor do they suffer from a somewhat paralysed limb. Some people may re-enter a house to check whether or not a stove has been turned off; but, having done so, that will be the end of the matter. The obsessional compulsive neurotic may return several times, knowing the irrationality of his behaviour, but unable to resist the compulsion to return because he is driven by a motive which is outside his awareness. This again is more like a qualitative distinction. The normal person does not feel a slight compulsion to return a second and a third time.

Phobic symptoms perhaps present a more difficult problem. It may be that Freud's (1936) distinction between rational fear and irrational anxiety applies here. There seem to be no grounds for calling a fear of snakes a neurotic symptom in someone who cannot distinguish between snakes which are dangerous and those which are not. Fear of heights may be utterly irrational or it may be an excessive reaction to moderate danger. In the latter instance this reaction is likely to occur in other mildly dangerous situations. It may be important to distinguish the first as a neurotic symptom and the second as a dysthymic state.

If the psychoanalysts are right in thinking that symptoms are a breakthrough in disguised form of previously repressed attitudes or impulses, this would involve personal discontinuity as observed by others and as experienced by the self. The observer could be saying "my friend now sometimes behaves in ways which I have not been led to expect from my past experience of him". The neurotic could be thinking "recently I have had experiences which are alien to what I have always thought I was. In some respects at least I no longer know what or who I am". "Why do I behave like this?" gives way to "What makes me behave like this?" The emphasis is on irrational change which is not understood. It is not understood because the behaviour is unconsciously motivated. To this extent the individual has lost the ability to intend his own actions.

The best way for the lay person to predict what another person will do is to ask him what he intends to do and then to try to assess the force of other agents which might come into conflict with this intention. The normal person may, indeed, say "I intend to do X; but I may fail because of a, b or c." Because of repeated failures in the past in similar situations, the neurotic individual may be forced into thinking, as it were, "I intend to do X; but I know I won't", which is absurd. We cannot intend to do something we *know* we will not do. Since the neurotic may be completely unaware of some powerful motive which is likely to thwart his intention, he cannot disclose part of the important information required for prediction by the observer. It follows that the ability of another person to understand, or predict, the afflicted individual's attitudes, motives and above all actions is greatly diminished. Part of the skill of the psychiatrist or clinical psychologist should lie in his ability to overcome this disadvantage. This he should be able to do through his repeated observations of somewhat similar responses to somewhat similarly construed stimuli by somewhat similar people. This entails diagnosis, however much the followers of Rogers, Kelly and others may protest to the contrary. The converse of the neurotic's dilemma might be a more insightful statement of their practice—"I *intend not* to use diagnosis; but I *know* I will".

Inevitably the neurotic's potentiality for entering into and maintaining mutual personal relationships is much reduced by the disability we have discussed. This is so whether the "You" in the "You and I" relationship is friend or psychologist. If the latter considers he is in mutual personal relationship with a patient at the beginning of treatment, he is treating someone who is not ill; if this comes about late in the treatment, he has cured him—or time was on his side.

A state may be conceived of as a more persistent, but not immutable, mood. Moods may be up, as in elation, or down, as in anxiety or depression. This seems to be more in the nature of a quantitative variation, since such moods are experienced in some degree, at some time and for some duration by everyone. Although we have included states of elation within the universe of discourse of personal illness, those who experience such states alone, without delusions of grandeur or extreme hyperactivity, only rarely present as patients.

Since a term is required to cover all three states and since they are, in fact, all disorders of mood, the term "dysthymic" states cannot be gainsaid, despite its well-established usage in a somewhat different sense (Eysenck, 1947).

There are many people who do not experience neurotic symptoms, in the sense used here, but who are especially vulnerable to periodic abnormal moods or states. There is a change from their habitual selves; but the change is more understandable and less irrational than is the case with neurotic symptoms. To the observer these dysthymic bouts seem rather characteristic of the person he knows. To the sufferer there is at least a lesser feeling of alienation from his usual self. "This is how I am for better or for worse." Their own character structure contributes greatly to the production of a psychological environment, and particularly of personal relationships, which from time to time become unendurable to both parties. Compared with psychotics and neurotics, they are little driven by unconscious motives and are, therefore, relatively well able to intend their own actions; but they are frequently thwarted by the intentions of others or by external circumstances which they have helped to bring about. As one patient unintentionally let slip, "I would be perfectly all right, if only my husband would do as I say".

Those who experience a dysthymic state alone are usually more readily aware of the external, or internal, stimuli which provoked the state. A woman, who had been diagnosed as a free-floating anxiety state, gave story after story on the Thematic Apperception Test of quarrels between a man and a woman. The psychologist, believing that the woman was fully aware of what she was communicating, asked for how long she and her husband had not been getting on together. He was taken aback when she swung round in her chair and said, "Who told you?" Clearly she was well aware of the psychological situation which had originally provoked her anxiety; but she was not aware of having communicated this knowledge.

If awareness of one's own attitudes and motives is less with neurotics than with dysthymic states, then the intensiveness of treatment and the skill required to carry it out may be much greater.

There is a widespread belief that this rather amorphous class of patients who suffer only from states is on the increase or, perhaps more likely, is seen more frequently by psychiatrists and clinical psychologists. That the more clear-cut neuroses are on the decrease is more debatable.

Our findings suggest that they are still frequent, but that psychiatrists often tend to diagnose anxiety or depressive state when obsessional, phobic or hysterical symptoms are present in equal degree (Foulds and Bedford, 1975).

The difficulty is clearly expressed by Wheelis (1969):

> Since our culture does not enforce the suppression of neurosis, one is more free to acknowledge the difficulty and to seek help . . . as the social attitude towards neurosis has changed, the patterns of neurosis have themselves undergone a change of equal magnitude . . . symptom neurosis was understood as a breakthrough in distorted form of a previously repressed impulse. The neurosis appeared as a phobia, an obsession, a compulsion, or as a physical symptom without a physical cause; was characterized by a definite, and often sudden, onset; and occurred in the setting of a relatively well-integrated and adequately functioning personality. It had the quality of a syndrome or illness. Diagnosis was relatively easy . . . In contrast, the frequently encountered character disorder of today cannot be adequately understood as the eruption of a previously repressed impulse; for the defensive warping of character is apt to loom larger and prove more troublesome than the erupting impulse. The conflict is less likely to manifest itself in the form of specific symptoms or to have the quality of a syndrome, but is vague and amorphous, pervading the entire personality . . . Diagnosis becomes increasingly difficult.

In the terminology used here, Wheelis appears to be describing individuals with a personality disorder who, under stress, develop a diffuse reactive state of anxiety or of depression, but who do not develop neurotic symptoms. The diagnostic difficulty resides partly in the relationship between the relatively enduring attributes of the personality and the more ephemeral dysthymic states. However that may be, few would deny that phobic, hysterical and obsessional neuroses together make up a smaller proportion of all neuroses as traditionally described. This accords with the idea that symptoms are rarer than states, that they are more challenging to our understanding and more dramatic in their manifestations and, consequently, are given much more space in textbooks than could be justified on the basis of frequency of occurrence alone.

Since our results (see Chapter 5) indicate that virtually all neurotics are also dysthymic states (whereas not all dysthymic states are neurotics), it will be important to try to determine whether the dysthymic states which occur together with neurotic symptoms are identical with those dysthymic states which occur alone.

Where neurotic symptoms and dysthymic states co-exist, there are four feasible relationships between them: (1) They are functionally independent; (2) the state is a reaction to the symptom; (3) the symptom serves to reduce the intensity of the state; (4) the development of the symptom indicates that the individual could no longer hold the line, as it were, at the lower state level. Here there need be no implication of a reduction in the intensity of the state.

Where the two conditions are independent, one might expect that treatment would alleviate the lesser state, for the reasons outlined above.

Where the state was a reaction to the major disruption brought about by the symptoms, one would predict that symptoms and states would diminish together.

Where the symptoms served to reduce the intensity of the state, removal of the symptom might lead to an at least temporary exacerbation of the state, which would then require to be treated. The same sequence would probably be required where there was no necessary implication of an exacerbation of the state.

The third possibility—that the symptom serves to reduce the state—is apparently acceptable to behaviour therapists as well as to psychoanalysts. "Often compulsive thoughts or rituals appear to be avoidance responses in so far as their performance reduces anxiety while attempts to resist them lead to an increase in anxiety" (Meyer and Chesser, 1970). A similar interpretation was put forward by Wolpe (1964). "Obsessive-compulsive rituals . . . may be maintained by reducing the anxiety generated by diverse conditioning stimuli."

As mentioned earlier, Berrington et al. (op. cit.) found evidence of a prodromal state of depression in the majority of patients who developed the symptom of a fugue. Presumably this dissociation was thought to serve the function of obliterating from awareness the conditions which originally brought about the state of depression.

The belle indifférence of conversion hysterics would be thought to serve the same reductive function, although it must be remembered that this symptom refers solely to the attitude to the conversion symptom and not to the patient's general condition. Most hysterics are, in fact, found to have diffuse states of anxiety or depression (see Chapter 5).

Thus, in ruminative, compulsive, dissociative, conversion and, presumably, phobic conditions, the major symptoms are seen as partially or temporarily successful defences against states.

That successful treatment of the major symptom can leave the lesser state relatively intact is well illustrated by the much-quoted case of the

18-year-old hand-washer (Wolpe, *op. cit.*). According to Eysenck and Rackman (1965),

> The excessive hand-washing was provoked by the patient's fear of contamination by urine. . . . The therapist's analysis of the patient's history led him to the conclusion that the fear of urine contamination was the basis of the obsessional neurosis, and it was decided to desensitize the patient to stimuli of this character.

They do not comment on the courageousness of a decision which entailed abandoning the cherished notion that the symptom (in this instance, the hand-washing) *is* the neurosis and that there is nothing underneath as it were (such as the fear of contamination by urine and, we learn, much more besides).

Thus, Wolpe himself mentions that "until the age of 15 Mr T had been made to share a bed with his sister, two years older, because she had a fear of being alone". This solicitousness for the daughter not unnaturally had unfortunate consequences for the son. "Having sexual responses to his sister made him feel very guilty and ashamed. He had become angry with his parents for imposing this on him and had hostile and at times destructive phantasies about them. He had been horrified at these, and had begun to regard himself as a despicable individual." Wolpe does not divulge whether the patient (or, indeed, he himself) was aware of any relationship between the sexual responses and the fear of contaminating himself with urine and, more particularly, others —among whom some of the bolder divergent thinkers might include his sister. Since all members of the family appear to have been breath-takingly innocent, may be the patient's sexual vocabulary was not up to paraphrasing Macbeth to ". . . . rather would this penis the multitudinous seas inseminate".

After recounting at considerable length the procedure adopted to desensitize the patient to urine, Wolpe produces, in his final sentence, the succinct throwaway line: "During the latter stages measures were also applied to overcome sexual and social anxieties." He does not state whether the measures were behavioural or whether the sexual and social anxieties increased *pari passu* with the removal of the hand-washing symptom. These were presumably the anxieties which were being reduced by the compulsive ritual. It does appear, at least, that the state outlasted the "symptom".

We can now summarize the differences between neurotic symptoms and dysthymic states which have been discussed.

	Symptoms	States
1. Difference from normal experience	qualitative	quantitative
2. Unconscious motives etc. implicated	more	less
3. Ability to intend one's own actions	less	greater
4. Ability of another to understand	less	greater
5. Ability to maintain personal relationships	less	greater
6. Depth and skill of treatment required	greater	less
7. Frequency in general and out-patient populations	less	greater
8. Frequency in day-patient and hospital populations	greater	less
9. Relationship between them	inclusive	exclusive
10. Effect of treatment where co-existent, and		
a. independent	removed second	removed first
b. state reactive to symptom	improve together	
c. state reduced by symptom	removed first	exacerbated
d. symptom evidence of increased disability	removed first	not exacerbated

Further consideration of the hierarchy of classes of personal illness

In Chapter 1, personal illness was described as the specifically human illness. It refers primarily to an adverse change in the ability to relate to other persons and in the ability to intend one's own actions. This change is so distressing, either to the experiencing individual or to others, that he or they seek help to bring about a reversal of that change.

In Chapter 2 it was suggested that the greater the change in these respects the more severe the illness and that, within the universe of discourse, one can usefully think of a hierarchy of classes in terms of increasing degrees of inability consciously to determine one's own future.

Elsewhere (Foulds, 1965) it was argued that the classes of personal illness could best be thought of as a succession of inclusive relationships, which could be described as "the King Lear principle". When Kent was trying to persuade the king to take shelter from the storm, Lear replied:

> Thou think'st 'tis much that this contentious storm
> invades us to the skin: so 'tis to thee;
> but where the greater malady is fix'd
> the lesser is scarce felt. . . .

The greater malady in Lear's case was, of course, his reaction to the ingratitude and cruelty of his daughters. Though the relationship between this and the storm is not strictly an inclusive one, it was considered an appropriate illustration to the extent that the major "illness" overrode or masked the minor. Orme (1971) has pointed out that the difficulty is that some schizophrenics do not appear to be neurotic; but what is being suggested is that, in spite of appearances, they are neurotic and that the explanation for this false appearance lies in the masking effect of "the greater malady". The woman who complained to the General Post Office that she had become pregnant since they put up a telegraph pole opposite her house, would just not be asked if she had a feeling of tension in the back of her neck.

Members of the most severely ill class suffer from delusions which indicate that there has been a very considerable disintegration of the self-concept. The individual believes that the thoughts in his head are not his thoughts or that someone else's emotions are being felt in his body or that his body has seemed to move about without his having any control over it. Those who suffer from delusions of passivity or influence usually also suffer from thought process disorder and/or incongruity or flatness of affect.

Thought process disorder refers to disorders of the actual process of thinking rather than to the content of thought. This may take the form of neologisms or an incorrect use of known words, as in: "They are hallucinated to each other, illusioned on each other". It may involve bizarre illogical modes of thought, such as: "They are white people who have been turned into coloured people. When it's daylight they'll think it is darkness" or "The man is trying to understand the woman by passing his right hand across his eyes" or "What she has asked is unheard of. He can't do anything because he is not listening". Or again he may suffer from thought-blocking, where his flow of talk is suddenly halted and he appears to go "blank". During these episodes they may suffer "transient confusions of identity" (Chapman and McGhie, 1964).

Incongruity of affect refers to the expression of emotions which would be regarded by most people as utterly inappropriate to the situation. It is as though the patient were responding to a totally different stimulus, as indeed he may conceivably be. Catatonic schizophrenics in remission have claimed that they were thinking of something other than that which was the ostensible subject of conversation. This rather unconvincing explanation, itself evidence of a failure in communication, may, however, be an *ex post facto* rationalization to justify their apparently bizarre behaviour.

Flatness of affect refers to a condition in which the patient gives no sign that he is experiencing any emotion in situations in which one would expect some emotion to be expressed. It may be objected that a non-integrated psychotic who suffers from flatness of affect cannot at the same time manifest a state of anxiety or depression; but it should be remembered that flatness of affect refers to the lack of *expression* of emotion by facial expression, tone of voice etc. and not to the failure to *experience* emotion. It is quite possible for a patient who does not manifest any sign of affect to acknowledge, for example on a questionnaire, that he does feel anxious or depressed, a point made by Priest *et al.* (1973).

It was suggested (Foulds, 1965) that these three clinical signs—non-integrated delusions, thought process disorder and flatness or incongruity of affect—were secondary to a disorder of personal relationships which involves withdrawal without the intention of, or motivation for, returning to action, particularly to communication with others. As McPherson *et al.* (1971b) comment,

> The ability to enter into, and sustain, such relationships must clearly depend in part upon his being able to discriminate, evaluate and make predictions about the feelings, motives and attitudes of himself and others: in other words, he must possess a stable system for construing "psychological" events. McPherson *et al.* (1971a) have suggested that the infrequent use of "psychological" constructs, as on Dixon's task (Dixon, 1968), and their use in an uncorrelated and inconsistent manner, as on the Bannister-Fransella test (1967), both indicate the absence in a patient of a stable system of this sort. It is interesting therefore that all three of the clinical signs which, according to Foulds, characterize "non-integrated psychosis" have been found to be associated with abnormal performance on either the Bannister-Fransella or Dixon tasks, i.e. thought-process disorder by Bannister (1960; 1962), Bannister and Fransella (1966) and Foulds *et al.* (1967); affective flattening by Dixon (1968), McPherson *et al.* (1970a; 1970b) and Rush (1970); and delusions of "non-integration" by McPherson (1969) and by the present study.

Moreover Bannister and Salmon (1966) and McPherson and Buckley (1970c) have shown that thought process disordered schizophrenics manifest less disorder on the Bannister-Fransella test when ranking constructs referring to physical attributes than when using "psychological" attributes.

Since performance on the Dixon task has been found to be abnormal in scarcely any manics or psychotic depressives (Blackburn, 1972), it would appear that the infrequent use of "psychological" constructs is virtually specific to schizophrenics and, therefore, probably to subjects with delusions of disintegration.

The position with regard to the Bannister-Fransella task is perhaps more equivocal. Bannister and Fransella (1966) found both Intensity (assessed by the strength of the correlations between constructs) and Consistency (assessed by the similarity in the pattern of construct inter-correlations between first and second grids) differentiated clinically thought disordered schizophrenics from clinically non-thought disordered schizophrenics, organics, depressives, neurotics and normals. McPherson et al. (1973) showed that thought disordered schizophrenics could be distinguished from non-thought disordered schizophrenics and from manics and psychotic depressives on both measures. Mellsop et al. (1971), however, found that only Intensity discriminated between thought disordered schizophrenics and manics. Breakey and Goodell (1972) criticize their study for having compared thought disordered schizophrenics with non-thought disordered manics. Mellsop et al. (op. cit.) were, however, presumably taking the generally accepted view that not all schizophrenics are thought process disordered, but that all the thought process disordered are schizophrenic. In such a case their methodology was correct. There is no thought disordered manic group which can possibly exist and, indeed, thought disorder is not among the criteria for a diagnosis of mania used by Breakey and Goodell themselves. If clinically it were thought that both manics and schizophrenics could be thought process disordered, there would be no ground for expecting the Grid Test to differentiate between manics and schizophrenics; but there is a very substantial consensus of psychiatric opinion that there is a form of thought disorder which is specific to schizophrenia. This is not at issue. If clinically thought disordered schizophrenics were compared with non-thought disordered manics and the Grid Test results showed no significant difference, then and only then could one conclude that the test is not one of thought process disorder as understood clinically.

What Breakey and Goodell did, however, in their own study was to compare manics and all schizophrenics, whether they were considered clinically to be thought disordered or not. Though the means on Intensity and Consistency of the schizophrenics were more in the thought disordered direction than the means of the manics, the differences were not statistically significant. They concluded that the Grid Test "is of no value in making a diagnosis between" schizophrenia and mania. Since Bannister has not claimed that all schizophrenics are thought disordered, their results are inconclusive. Nevertheless they did obtain the very surprising finding that 36% of their manics and 23% of their normals were thought disordered, using the dual Intensity-Consistency criterion advocated by Bannister. This is so much at odds with reasonable expectation and with the results of other studies that, in spite of the predilection of psychologists for giving credence to negative over positive results, it requires cross-validation.

Taken as a whole we do not consider that the findings are an embarrassment to the claim that loss of awareness of the self as agent (manifested in delusions of passivity), thought process disorder and flatness or incongruity of affect may each be a sufficient, and the presence of at least one a necessary, condition for the diagnosis of non-integrated psychosis (Foulds, 1965).

Jaspers (1963) believes that the passivity phenomenon precedes the thought and affective disorders. Henderson and Gillespie (1946) incline to the view that the affective disorder precedes the thought process disorder. The indication appears, therefore, to be that passivity is primary and has as a later consequence affective flattening or incongruity, which, in turn, has as a consequence thought process disorder. This, however, leaves the passivity phenomenon unexplained.

An attempt to account for the three phenomena was made (Foulds, 1965) by speculating that an excessive fear of personal relationships resulted in withdrawal without the intention of, or motivation for, returning to participation in such relationships. It is of interest to note in this connection that Williams and Quirke (1972) found, *inter alia*, that their "results suggest that rated withdrawal, particularly on the Wing scale, may be more closely related to use of psychological constructs than either rated thought disorder or affective flattening. These latter two did correlate with psychological construing, but not so highly". Later they comment that

hospitalization and age (in the schizophrenic group only) also correlated with amount of psychological construing. The findings of Wing and Brown (1970) can probably best explain this cluster of correlations. They found that poverty of the social environment correlated highly with social withdrawal, flattening of affect and poverty of speech, but not with incoherence of speech or coherently expressed delusions, and suggested that the direction of causality was from environment to symptom. Assuming that old and frequently hospitalized patients would tend to be in a socially poverty-stricken environment, and that a lack of social stimulation would lead to a cessation of efforts to construe socially (i.e. psychologically) by individuals, then the occurrence of these correlations becomes more easily comprehensible.

Prisoners are in a lamentably socially poverty-stricken environment, but very few become schizophrenic and they do have the intention of, or motivation for, returning to the world. Writers, painters and composers often retreat into a socially poverty-stricken environment in order to create. Schizophrenics retreat into a socially poverty-stricken environment and, *pace* Laing, do not create. Theirs is a self-imposed isolation from their fellows (as distinct from the isolation imposed by the experimenter in sensory deprivation experiments and accepted as a temporary measure by the subject) and this, we speculated, was primary. Repeated *avoidance* of exposure to the language and emotions of other people could lead to loss of awareness of oneself as the agent of one's own actions, since one would be utterly preoccupied with one's own thoughts and thought without communication can determine nothing. Having virtually removed the possibility of validating one's thoughts and emotions, it is not unreasonable to suppose that what we know as thought process disorder and flattening or incongruity of affect would follow. In other words, it is the schizophrenic who is the prototypical Kellyan, a spectator excluded from participation in what he contemplates, barely participating in existence.

Chapman (*op. cit.*), however, takes the contrary view, namely that it is the schizophrenic's extreme inability to communicate, which he believes has an organic basis, which leads to withdrawal. Although by no means all who suffer from a form of organic pathology which leads to difficulty in communicating withdraw in the way that schizophrenics do, the present view and that of Chapman must remain speculative.

The statement that the non-integrated psychotic class is inclusive of the integrated psychotic class implies that the non-integrated psychotic is non-integrated only in some respects and that he will in fact share with members of the integrated psychotic class that characteristic which is being regarded as pathognomic for that class, namely the presence of delusions which imply a grossly distorted self-concept. Any member of the non-integrated psychotic class should, therefore, manifest delusions of grandeur and/or contrition and/or persecution. These, in Rosenzweig's terms (1934) are respectively impunitive, intropunitive and extrapunitive delusions. These are all inadequate methods of dealing with frustration or conflict. The grandiose delusion may be seen as an attempt to leave the field, to pretend that there is no frustration or conflict, or that even if there were it would be overcome. It should, therefore, occasion little surprise if such sufferers do, in fact, sometimes complain of states of anxiety or depression—though not as frequently as most other groups. The delusion of contrition may be seen as an attempt to confess to others and oneself for the wrong crime in order to block enquiry into their covert "real" crime, extrapunitiveness. They are perhaps, in other words, being intropunitive about their extrapunitiveness. Paranoid psychotics are sometimes regarded as the reverse of the depressive psychotics' coin. This might suggest that they, rather than projecting their hostility on to others, are being extrapunitive about their intropunitiveness. It may, therefore, be that the function of the delusion of persecution is to avert self-blame. It certainly often appears to be the case that the paranoid individual cannot tolerate any criticism.

Frequently, in the non-integrated psychotic, integrated delusions take on a more bizarre colouring, as in the young man with the grandiose delusion that he had knocked God off his throne and was perplexed about how He would manage to get back on—a feat which normal believers would be unlikely to regard as beyond the capabilities of the Deity. A popular interpretation today would no doubt be that only an obtuse psychologist would fail to recognize that the young man was a mystic experiencing The Dark Night of the Soul. Like schizophrenic art, which does not look much like art unless the individual was an artist before his illness, schizophrenic experiencing to most non-Laingians is unlikely to seem much like mysticism unless the individual was a mystic before his illness. To attribute preternatural powers to schizophrenics is a fashionable form of protest against the constraints and follies of human society. It can pose as a life-enhancing movement only by repression and denial of the fact of the disintegration of the person in schizophrenia. In those with a professional obligation to try to understand, care for and treat this tragic condition such quixotry seems fundamentally irresponsible.

If the integrated psychotic class is inclusive of the neurotic class, then any member of the integrated psychotic class (which will include members of the non-integrated psychotic class) will manifest dissociative and/or conversion and/or phobic and/or compulsive and/or ruminative symptoms.

If the neurotic class is inclusive of the dysthymic state class (and this will include both non-integrated and integrated psychotics) any member should manifest an anxiety and/or a depressive and/or an elated state.

We have contended that those who wish entirely to abolish diagnosis in psychiatry are reminiscent of the manic who answered "No" to an enquiry as to whether she ever decorated herself with flowers at the precise moment that she was doing just that. Nevertheless, when a new form of classification is being advanced, even a more sympathetic audience will wish to know what practical difference the new form would make.

The main arguments advanced against psychiatric diagnosis are that: (1) it implies a disease entity model; (2) it cannot be arrived at reliably; (3) it has no implications for treatment; (4) it has no prognostic implications.

(1) Although historically psychiatric diagnosis has frequently been associated with a disease entity model, such an association is not inevitable. Indeed, as Hill (1968) has pointed out,

> It is evident that for 3,000 years western medical thought has been dominated by two major contrasting concepts of disease. . . . The first view is that of disease as a separate distinct entity. . . . The second and alternative view of disease presents it as a deviation from normal. In this concept, the platonic variety, the healthy man falls ill through the influence of any number of factors, physical or psychological, and, as a consequence, "is changed and suffers". The change in him and the suffering he experiences is then his disease.

In Hill's opinion this second view has been gaining ground since the latter part of the nineteenth century.

Our proposed hierarchy model clearly fits more happily within the platonic view and does not necessitate acceptance of a disease entity model. It may, indeed, make acceptance of such a model more difficult. We will be proposing, for example, that individuals in the course of recovery from their personal illness move from one class to another, though not in a random way. This movement is more difficult to accommodate within a disease entity model.

(2) We contend that reliability studies have been in error in considering the relationship between any two classes, or any two groups in

different classes, as being of an either and/or type. This is the appropriate relationship between groups within classes only. The hierarchy model proposes that the relationship between any two classes is an inclusive one and that membership in a group within a class higher in the hierarchy overrides membership in a group lower in the hierarchy. Thus, if it be agreed that a patient has an anxiety state and compulsive symptoms, there is no need to decide which is the principal diagnosis. Compulsive symptoms belong in a higher class in the hierarchy than anxiety states. The former, therefore, take precedence. This reduction in decision making should raise interjudge reliabilities.

Reliability studies which rely on single judgments made at different times are of no value as such within the hierarchy model, since subjects quite often change their class within a matter of weeks. Within the disease entity model, this can only mean that one of the diagnoses was "wrong"; within the hierarchy model, this change simply records an improvement or deterioration in the patient's condition. To establish diagnostic reliability, it would, therefore, be necessary to have at least two raters on each occasion. If they agreed on the same diagnosis on each occasion, the diagnosis is reliable and the condition unchanged; if they agreed on a different diagnosis on each occasion, the diagnoses are reliable, but the condition has changed. Again, within the disease entity model, this can only mean that one of the diagnoses, though reliable, was "wrong".

(3 and 4) If a subject is deemed to be suffering from a psychotic depression, he is usually treated with ECT or an anti-depressant drug. The outcome is then assessed in terms of the degree of amelioration of his psychotic depression. We find, however, that approximately half of such patients complain, *inter alia*, of phobias. If, as seems usually to be the case, these phobias outlast the psychotic depression, it may be that the treatment should change to some form of, say, behaviour therapy.

Within the hierarchy model the outcome question is not simply how much better the psychotic depression is, but how far down the hierarchy the patient has moved. He could still be suffering from certain neurotic symptoms and dysthymic states, or from certain states only, or from neither symptoms nor states.

The implications for both treatment and outcome within the hierarchy model differ, therefore, from those within the more traditional models.

Summary

A brief review of the literature indicates that a number of psychiatrists and psychologists have entertained the notion of a hierarchy of classes of psychiatric, or personal, illness. This has generally been implicit rather than explicit and has rarely encompassed the whole range of illnesses. The time, therefore, seemed ripe for a systematic attempt to do just this and to incorporate replicable measurements. These will be described in the next chapter.

It was found necessary to take states of anxiety, of depression and of elation out of the neurotic class and to form a separate class of dysthymic states. A number of differentiae were proposed in order to try to justify this change. The most important of these differentiae is that all, or virtually all, obsessionals, phobics and hysterics manifest states of anxiety and/or of depression and/or of elation; whereas, by no means all anxiety, depressive or elated states suffer from obsessional, phobic or hysterical symptoms.

The four classes to be considered are, therefore, dysthymic states, neurotics, integrated and non-integrated psychotics. It is claimed that the mildest type of personal illness is the dysthymic state. Those who experience such states, however intensely, are relatively well able to intend their own actions and thoughts, and to choose their course of conduct. They are, therefore, more able than members of the other classes to enter into, and sustain, mutual personal relationships.

Those who suffer from neurotic symptoms are considered to be more severely ill because their behaviour, in limited areas of their lives, is more completely determined by motives outside their awareness and control. Provided they are not also personality deviants, their egocentricity—which is a feature of all the personally ill—will take the form of excessive preoccupation with their own difficulties rather than with a conscious desire to manipulate others. This pre-occupation will itself, however, restrict and put great strain upon their personal relationships.

Integrated psychotics are deemed to be still more severely ill because their entire concept of themselves has become grossly distorted and more of their behaviour tends to be determined by unconscious motives. Such delusional thinking leads to behaviour which constitutes an almost insuperable barrier to satisfying personal relationships. The highly encapsulated delusions of some paranoid psychotics may appear to put them closer in some respects to neurotics than to psychotics; but, when they do enter the delusional area, they are generally less comprehensible to the average person and thus set up more formidable barriers to personal relationships.

Finally, non-integrated psychotics are seen as the most severely ill because they no longer know who they are and feel that their behaviour is fully determined by forces outside their control. They have virtually ceased to be persons and cannot, therefore, enter into mutual personal relationships. There is a minority of patients who do feel that they are in control of their own actions; but this takes such a bizarre form (e.g., the young man knocking God off his throne) that no one can give them credence and the barriers to mutual personal relationships are equally formidable.

These are suggested stages along a road to personal disintegration. Some will travel only to the first stage; others will go the whole way and, in so doing, will incorporate within their experience all the intervening stages. Where the greater malady is fixed, the lesser should be noted and subsequently treated.

It is claimed that the proposed hierarchical system of classification provides a more cohesive structure than other systems and that it has implications for diagnostic reliability, treatment and outcome which are different from those of a disease entity model and which warrant investigation.

5

Investigation of the Hierarchy with the Delusions-Symptoms-States Inventory

The Delusions-Symptoms-States Inventory

INTRODUCTION

In this chapter the Delusions-Symptoms-States Inventory will be described and the data gathered on it will be related to the hierarchy hypothesis.

The DSSI differs from its predecessor, the Symptom-Sign Inventory (Foulds and Hope, 1968), in being somewhat more descriptive than diagnostic. Although psychiatric diagnosis has been formally abandoned as the outside criterion for the allocation of items to traditional syndromes, the items were intended to be representative of the salient features of particular clinical conditions.

The items are divided into four classes and twelve sets of seven items each (Foulds and Bedford, 1975). We are concerned in the first part of the chapter with the sets, which are: delusions of Disintegration (dD); of Persecution (dP); of Grandeur (dG) and of Contrition (dC); Conversion symptoms (CVs); Dissociative symptoms (Ds); Phobic symptoms (Ps); Compulsive symptoms (CPs) and Ruminative symptoms (Rs); states of Anxiety (sA); of Depression (sD); and of Elation (sE).

In the case of the non-delusional sets, the descriptive terms for the sets are the same as the clinical condition, with the exception of state of Elation, which probably denotes Hypomania. It was thought that delusions of Disintegration would be more or less equivalent to Schizophrenia, delusions of Persecution to Paranoid Psychosis, delusions of

Grandeur to Mania and delusions of Contrition to Psychotic Depression.

In the condition which is generally described as grandiose paranoia, the delusions of grandeur are often thought to be secondary to and explanatory of the delusions of persecution. "I have been singled out to be persecuted, so I must be a very important person." In mania the delusions of grandeur are primary and the patient is much more impervious to the attitudes of others. It was considered, therefore, that, given a forced choice, most psychiatrists and clinical psychologists would allocate delusions of grandeur to mania rather than to paranoia and that grandiose paranoids would score on both delusions of grandeur and of persecution.

A study was undertaken to ascertain what percentage of psychiatrists and clinical psychologists would agree with the allocation of the items to the particular clinical syndromes. The study is not, therefore, strictly a validation of the allocation of items to sets, but rather of the equivalence of sets and syndromes.

THE INVENTORY

The DSSI is currently being used as a self-report inventory, though this need not preclude its eventual use in semi-structured interview situations. There are two temporal versions—Most of My Life (ML) and Recently (R). Concern here is solely with the R form, in which all items begin with the word "Recently".

It has often been objected that sets containing as few as seven items cannot be reliable. This depends, of course, on the nature of the items. One item should be sufficient to obtain a reliable and valid estimate of the patient's name. If one asked the patient seven times to state all his names, again validity and reliability should be satisfactorily high. In other words, if the questions are sufficiently unambiguous and homogeneous, there can be a reasonable expectation that even a seven-item scale will be reliable. Similar points have been made by Comrey (1970) and their efficacy demonstrated.

The 84 items, although clearly not exhaustive, refer to a large part of the range of phenomena reported by patients and extensively described in the psychiatric literature. We have attempted to confine ourselves as far as possible to the primary, or essential, features, that is to those features without which the condition would not be nominated. Failure to do this has often resulted in the unnecessary lengthening of inventories. It has also weakened them, in the sense that many items are introduced which are common to many syndromes and thus create undesirable overlap between syndromes. This is especially the case when items are not restricted to symptoms and signs, but include precipitating events, age and personality characteristics.

Items answered "False" always scored 0. In nearly all instances in the eight sets comprising the Dysthymic States and Neurotic Symptoms classes, if the person affirms an item, he has additionally to indicate the extent to which he is distressed by it, e.g. a bit, a lot or almost unbearably. Occasionally, particularly for the state of Elation items, he indicates instead the frequency of occurrence, e.g. seldom, often or nearly always. It is manifestly inappropriate to ask someone who has said that recently he has been very excitedly happy, how much it has distressed him. Scores of 1, 2 and 3 are given to each endorsed item in the direction of greater distress or greater frequency.

Neither the degree of distress nor the frequency of occurrence is the criterion by which delusions are judged. It is rather the degree of conviction with which the false belief is held. A person affirming any delusional item, whether of the non-integrated or the integrated variety, has, therefore, to indicate the degree of his conviction, e.g. not very sure, fairly sure or certain. These are likewise allotted scores of 1, 2 and 3.

PROCEDURE

Sixteen psychiatrists and nine clinical psychologists agreed to undertake the task of allocating the 84 items of the DSSI to the 12 syndromes or to a 13th (Other), if they felt that none of the given 12 was appropriate.

Each item was typed on a separate card with a number on the reverse side. The instructions for the subject were: "Please allocate each of the cards, by number, to one of the 12 syndromes below. Enter the item number against the syndrome that you think is appropriate or closest. Try to come to a choice for every item. Use the category 'Other' as little as possible."

RESULTS

In what follows "agreement" refers to agreement between the judges and the predicted allocation of items to clinical syndromes, unless otherwise stated. The DSSI set description is given first with the predicted syndrome second.

STATE OF ANXIETY—ANXIETY STATE

Average agreement over the set of seven items was 82% (87% for psychologists and 79% for psychiatrists). The highest agreement for any item was 96% and the lowest 64%. In the latter case, the remaining 36% opted for Neurotic Depression. This was much the commonest alternative chosen in this set; but a substantial majority of judges allocated all the items of the set in the predicted way.

STATE OF DEPRESSION—NEUROTIC DEPRESSION

Average agreement over the set was 47% (62% for psychologists and 39% for psychiatrists). The highest agreement for any item was 84% and the lowest 28%. For six out of the seven items a majority of judges allocated the item to Psychotic Depression. Clearly each of these symptoms (see Appendix A) does occur in Psychotic Depression; but, although we did not examine this, it is highly unlikely that any of the judges would have considered any of the items to be delusional. There was a marked difference here between clinical psychologists and psychiatrists. Whereas a majority of psychologists allocated five of the seven items to Neurotic Depression, a majority of psychiatrists allocated only one item in this way. In fact, only one of the entire 84 DSSI items is allocated by a majority to Neurotic Depression. One wonders how this diagnosis is made and made with such frequency.

STATE OF ELATION—HYPOMANIA

A similar situation prevails here. Average agreement over the set was 50% (65% for psychologists and 42% for psychiatrists). The highest agreement for any item was 76% and the lowest 8%). For three items the majority chose Mania (see Appendix A). Again, it seems unlikely that any of the judges would call any of these items delusional. Once again there appears to be a failure to distinguish between symptoms which, though occurring commonly in the condition, are not differentiae.

CONVERSION SYMPTOMS—CONVERSION HYSTERIA

Average agreement over the set was 74% (81% for psychologists and 70% for psychiatrists). The highest agreement for any item was 100% and the lowest 32%. This latter item (see Appendix A) was the only one in which a majority of judges agreed on its allocation to a syndrome other than Conversion Hysteria. The choice was Anxiety State. Our experience had led us to believe that a rather grotesque degree of shaking was characteristic of Hysterics; but we were either in error in this assumption or the wording did not bring out the excessive degree intended. This item apart, no other choice came anywhere near Conversion Hysteria.

DISSOCIATIVE SYMPTOMS—DISSOCIATIVE HYSTERIA

Average agreement over the set was 60% (62% for psychologists and 59% for psychiatrists). The highest agreement for any item was 96% (two items) and the lowest 20%. There were three instances in which a majority opted for something other than Dissociative Hysteria (see Appendix A). For items 48 and 60 the majority chose Schizophrenia, again presumably not intending "delusional". A slight majority allocated item 72 to Conversion Hysteria.

PHOBIC SYMPTOMS—PHOBIC DISORDER

Overall agreement was 73% (71% for psychologists and 74% for psychiatrists). The highest agreement for any item was 92% (three items) and the lowest 32% (two items). These were the only two in which a majority chose a syndrome other than Phobic Disorder, both were Obsessional ruminations (see Appendix A).

COMPULSIVE SYMPTOMS—OBSESSIONAL RITUALS

Overall agreement was 91% (92% for psychologists and 91% for psychiatrists). The highest agreement for any item was 100% (two items) and the lowest 68%. In all instances a clear majority chose Obsessional rituals, the weakest being 68% against 20% opting for Obsessional ruminations.

RUMINATIVE SYMPTOMS—OBSESSIONAL RUMINATIONS

Overall agreement was 63% (67% for psychologists and 61% for psychiatrists). The highest agreement for any item was 80% and the lowest 48% (two items). In both these latter instances, however, Obsessional ruminations was chosen twice as often as the most popular alternative. All items were, therefore, chosen in the predicted way.

DELUSIONS OF PERSECUTION—PARANOID DISORDER

Overall agreement for the set was 98% (100% for psychologists and 96% for psychiatrists). The highest agreement for any item was 100%

(three items) and the lowest 96% (the remaining four items). Clearly we can all recognize paranoia when we see it.

DELUSIONS OF GRANDEUR—MANIA

Overall agreement was 62% (60% for psychologists and 62% for psychiatrists). The highest agreement for any item was 88% and the lowest 28%. In this last instance, 40% opted for Schizophrenia. For item 81, equal numbers chose Schizophrenia and Mania (see Appendix A).

DELUSIONS OF CONTRITION—PSYCHOTIC DEPRESSION

Overall agreement was 93% (92% for psychologists and 95% for psychiatrists). The highest agreement for any item was 100% and the lowest 84%. When considered in conjunction with Neurotic Depression, it appears that most psychiatrists attribute virtually all "depressive" symptoms to Psychotic Depression and virtually none to Neurotic Depression.

DELUSIONS OF DISINTEGRATION—SCHIZOPHRENIA

Overall agreement was 81% (86% for psychologists and 79% for psychiatrists). The highest agreement for any item was 96% and the lowest 56% (the remaining 44% choosing Paranoid Disorder—see Appendix A). All items were, therefore, chosen in accordance with the prediction.

Altogether there were 17 items out of the 84 in which a majority chose differently from the original prediction. Of these 17, 11 involved allocating a non-delusional item to a psychotic group.

In nine out of the 12 sets psychologists agreed more closely than did psychiatrists with the original allocations; but in only three of these were the differences substantial.

The highest percentage of agreed items for any judge was 93 and the lowest was 57. The median was 70%.

SUMMARY AND CONCLUSIONS

Sixteen psychiatrists and nine clinical psychologists allocated each of the DSSI items to the most appropriate clinical syndrome.

A large majority of judges (with one exception at least two to one) allocated all the items of the following sets to what had originally been considered to be the appropriate clinical syndrome: state of Anxiety to Anxiety State; Compulsive symptoms to Obsessional Disorder (rituals);

Ruminative symptoms to Obsessional Disorder (ruminations); delusions of Persecution to Paranoid Disorder; delusions of Contrition to Psychotic Depression and delusions of Disintegration to Schizophrenia.

One item from the Phobic symptoms was allocated by a two to one majority to Anxiety State. Two items from the Phobic symptoms were allocated by a small majority to Obsessional Disorder (ruminations). One item from the delusions of Grandeur set was allocated equally to Mania and Schizophrenia and another, by a small majority, to Schizophrenia. Three items from the state of Elation set were allocated to Mania (two by a large majority). Two items from the Dissociative symptoms set were allocated by a large majority to Schizophrenia and one, by a small majority, to Conversion Hysteria. Finally, six items from the state of Depression set were allocated by small majorities to Psychotic Depression.

Overall, a majority of psychiatrists allocated 80% of items in accordance with prediction. The corresponding figure for clinical psychologists was 88%

The confusion over the diagnosis of psychotic and neurotic depression noted by Kreitman *et al.* (1961) appears again in this study. A majority of psychiatrists allocated only one item out of the 84 items of the DSSI to Neurotic Depression and yet this is almost certainly the commonest non-psychotic diagnosis in psychiatry. Had this view been adopted, not one of the 500-odd patients who have so far completed the DSSI would have been diagnosed as Neurotic Depression. The implicit argument must presumably be that six out of seven of our state of Depression items occur more commonly in psychotic than in neurotic depression, but that they are not in themselves sufficient to warrant a diagnosis of psychotic depression. This diagnosis is made only when these states occur in the presence of certain other symptoms, notably delusions of Contrition. If such were not the case, a diagnosis of Neurotic Depression would never be made; if such be the case, the diagnosis of Psychotic Depression should be made on the basis of these other symptoms, notably delusions of Contrition.

This argument is underlined by the fact that, when judges were asked simply to allocate each item to the most appropriate of the sets as described in the DSSI, there were only four instances out of the 84 in which less than 60% of judges allocated items to the set envisaged to be the appropriate one by the test constructors. In three of these four instances roughly twice as many judges agreed with the *a priori* set as with any other set. Thus, in only one instance did a majority of judges agree in allocating an item to a set other than the *a priori* one. It can, therefore, be concluded that, with this one exception, consensual validation for the allocation of items to sets was satisfactory.

The DSSI and psychiatric ratings

An additional study was carried out to ascertain to what extent DSSI scores agreed with psychiatric ratings for the presence of the relevant symptoms and states in 96 in-patients.

The raters ranged from trainee psychiatrists to consultants and the ratings were carried out during the course of normal clinical practice. They were asked to rate on a 4-point scale from 0 (not present) to 3 (where there was very definite evidence that the particular symptom was present).

As "delusions of Disintegration" is not a concept used by psychiatrists, this was broken down into its component parts—delusions of passivity, autochthonous delusions and hallucinations. It was clear from the ratings that some psychiatrists had misunderstood "passivity", since it was often rated as present in patients who were given a non-psychotic diagnosis. It was presumably interpreted by some to denote the personality characteristic of passivity. This has, therefore, been omitted. Ratings for autochthonous delusions and hallucinations were combined.

Table 1 shows the results of an analysis of variance for DDSI X Ratings. Since point 3 was rarely used, this was collapsed with point 2.

TABLE 1
DSSI scores and Ratings for 96 in-patients

Set	Rating categories	F	df	p
sA	0; 1; 2+	3·37	2,93	0·05
sD	0; 1; 2+	9·64	2,93	0·001
sE	0; 1; 2+	14·99	2,93	0·001
CVs	0; 1; 2+	3·51	2,93	0·05
Ds	0; 1; 2+	5·46	2,93	0·01
Ps	0; 1; 2+	1·07	2,93	n.s.
CPs	0; 1; 2+	0·90	2,93	n.s.
Rs	0; 1; 2+	0·36	2,93	n.s.
dP	0; 1; 2+	5·79	2,93	0·01
dG	0; 1; 2+	6·92	2,93	0·01
dC	0; 1; 2+	4·77	2,93	0·05
dD	0/1 v. 2+	7·05	1,94	0·01

There was thus a significant relationship between DSSI scores and psychiatric ratings for all groups, except those with Phobic, Compulsive and Ruminative symptoms. Since the ratings of senior psychiatrists were considerably closer to the DSSI scores than were those of junior psychiatrists, it seems safe to conclude that these senior psychiatrists were eliciting much the same symptomatology that the patients revealed in the DSSI.

In addition to rating for the presence or absence of sets of symptoms or states, the clinicians were asked to give overall diagnoses. These are difficult to compare with the DSSI "diagnosis". Sometimes no diagnosis was given (through omission rather than intent) and on other occasions diagnoses were given which were outside the scope of the DSSI, such as personality disorder, alcoholism, anorexia nervosa, sexual deviation, psychosomatic disorder. These diagnoses are different in kind from neurotic and psychotic diagnoses. It seems unfortunate to operate two systems of classification which are not mutually exclusive. We would prefer to see such diagnoses as "state of Depression with alcoholism", "Obsessional-compulsive neurosis with anorexia nervosa", "Hysterical Dissociative neurosis in a personality disorder", "Non-personally ill homosexual", "state of Anxiety with duodenal ulcer" etc. However, a comparison could be made in 68 cases. Of these 36 had been seen by consultants or other senior psychiatrists and 32 by registrars or below. For the senior psychiatrists, there was complete agreement with the DSSI in 42% of cases, partial agreement in 22% (e.g. Ruminative v. Compulsive Obsessional) and disagreement in 36%. For the junior psychiatrists, the corresponding figures were 9% full agreement, 34% partial agreement and 56% disagreement. Either experience counts for a great deal or modern diagnostic teaching is inadequate.

It was disturbing to find that 15% of cases were rated as *not* having delusions, but were given a psychotic diagnosis and 26% were rated as having delusions, but were given a neurotic diagnosis. For the purpose of validating the inventory, it is fortunately more appropriate to use clinical ratings rather than diagnoses arrived at by unspecified and seemingly different classificatory systems.

Investigation of the hierarchy hypothesis
INTRODUCTION

As a first step in examining responses to the DSSI(R) it was decided, in advance of the data, that a score of 4 or more on any of the seven-item sets should give reasonable confidence that the person "really had" symptoms within that set, or at least intended to convey that impression. To gain a score of 4 or more at least two items had to be affirmed. Strictly, when using categories, the presence of even one symptom should be sufficient to allocate a person to that category; but insistence on at least two symptoms allows to some extent for misreading or misinterpretation by the subject.

To test the hierarchy hypothesis a score of 1 was allocated to a person scoring 4 or more for any set of items within the Dysthymic States class and a 0 was given to a person *all* of whose scores fell below 4. This procedure was repeated at the next three class levels, i.e. those of Neurotic Symptoms, Integrated Delusions and Delusions of Disintegration. Each person's responses on the whole DSSI can then be summarized in terms of four scores, a 0 or a 1 for each of the four classes. Whilst there are 16 logically possible patterns that a person might obtain, only the following five conform to the hierarchical model (where $\overline{PI}$ = Not personally ill):

Name of pattern (by highest class)	Delusions of Disintegration (DD)	Integrated Delusions (ID)	Neurotic Symptoms (NS)	Dysthymic States (DS)
DD	1	1	1	1
ID	0	1	1	1
NS	0	0	1	1
DS	0	0	0	1
$\overline{PI}$	0	0	0	0

The hypothesis can now be expressed as: (a) any person scoring 1 for a class will also score 1 in *all* the lower classes; (b) where that person scores 0 for a class he will also score 0 in *all* the higher classes.

SUBJECTS

Data were collected on 253 patients in Canadian, English and Scottish psychiatric hospitals, within one week of admission in nearly all instances. The 118 out-patients were seen at their first appointment and the 109 day-patients within their first week of attendance. The total number was thus 480.

Suspected organics and illiterates were excluded from the study. Apart from these restrictions, each group may be considered representative of the particular ward or clinic.

The 234 normal subjects were all United Kingdom residents. All were non-graduate hospital personnel or attenders at recreational and educational classes. Given the easier access to younger groups and the known *Stürm und Drang* of adolescence (and, for some, the early twenties) reported on state-trait questionnaires (Eysenck and Eysenck, 1969; Philip, 1973), it was decided to divide the total group into those aged up to 21 years and those aged 22 years and above. The age and sex distributions of all subjects are shown in Table 2.

RESULTS

Table 2 shows the percentages of male and female in-patients, day-patients and out-patients falling into each of the five hierarchy patterns and the 11 non-hierarchy patterns (here combined as "Other patterns"). As normal subjects were expected to score predominantly as "non-personally ill", their results are presented primarily for comparison.

TABLE 2

Percentage of male and female patients and normals falling into each of the five hierarchy patterns and other patterns

| | | Age | | Hierarchy Classes | | | | | | |
	n	Mean	s.d.	1111 DD	0111 ID	0011 NS	0001 DS	0000 $\overline{\text{PI}}$	Other patterns	% fitting hierarchy
Patients										
In-male	111	34·3	12·2	14·4	21·6	27·0	17·1	11·7	8·1	91·9
female	142	33·0	12·1	7·0	25·3	26·8	15·5	16·9	8·5	91·5
Day-male	45	34.3	11·8	11·1	11·1	46·7	13·3	15·6	2·2	97·8
female	64	33·9	11·5	6·3	15·6	46·9	17·2	10·9	3·1	96·9
Out-male	59	34·9	13·9	5·1	11·9	39·0	16·9	20·3	6·8	93·2
female	59	31·6	11·4	1·7	16·9	37·3	28·8	8·5	6·8	93·2
Total	480			8·1	19·2	34·2	17·7	14·2	6·7	93·3
Normals										
21 yrs— m	24	19·7	1·2	0	0	4·2	8·3	79·2	8·3	91·7
f	74	19·2	1·2	0	0	9·5	8·1	75·7	6·8	93·2
22 yrs+ m	36	30·2	9·1	0	2·8	0	5·6	88·9	2·8	97·2
f	100	34·1	9·5	0	0	2·0	6·0	87·0	5·0	95·0
Total	234			0	0·4	4·3	6·8	83·3	5·5	94·5

The Dysthymic State of Elation is not scored for non-patient groups. To agree with statements such as "Recently life could not have been better *in any way*" may reflect a Panglossian optimism about life and world events, but scarcely psychopathology. In those undergoing psychiatric treatment such elation is discordant and abnormal. State of

Elation is unique among the DSSI syndromes in this respect of having different implications for normal and patient populations. At the empirical level, it is a reasonable generalization to say that state of Elation, when it occurs, is found in isolation among non-patients and as part of a multiple syndrome picture among patients.

It can be seen that the lowest level of agreement with the hierarchy among psychiatric patients is 91·5%; whilst the highest is 97·8%. For all six patient groups combined the concordance rate is 93·3%.

A similar percentage of normal subjects produced patterns conforming to the hierarchy. In their case this reassuringly means a major preponderance of the non-personally ill class.

As anticipated, the younger normals more often produced personal illness patterns than did their elders, virtually all being confined, however, to the two lowest classes.

It is noteworthy that the percentage falling into the Delusions of Disintegration class is much higher among males than among females and that the percentage decreases as one moves from in-patients through day-patients to out-patients.

The percentage of cases falling into the Integrated Delusions class is, however, consistently somewhat higher among females than among males. Whilst the percentage is much higher among in-patients, day-patients and out-patients do not differ in this respect.

The percentage of cases falling into the Neurotic Symptoms class is closely similar in all types of patients settings for males and females. The percentage is highest among day-patients, being almost twice as high as among in-patients.

The only outstanding group within the Dysthymic States class is female out-patients, where the percentage is considerably higher. This is compensated for, as it were, by the very small percentage of female out-patients, compared with male, who fall into the "Not-personally ill" class.

The base rate problem is exceedingly complex in this particular study. Perhaps the best one can do is to look at the number of cases who have Delusions of Disintegration who have and who do not have Integrated Delusions and compare this with the number of cases who have Neurotic Symptoms (except for those with Delusions of Disintegration also) and who do have and who do not have Integrated Delusions. The strictest disease entity model might go so far as to predict that none of those with Delusions of Disintegration and none of those with Neurotic Symptoms would have Integrated Delusions. A more middle-of-the-road approach would presumably predict that some would have Integrated Delusions and some would not, without being able to be any more specific.

In this study, of those who fell into Class 4, 38 (or 88%) also fell into Class 3, but 5 (or 12%) did not. Of those who fell into Class 2 (other than Class 4s) 89 (or 36%) fell into Class 3 and 158 (or 64%) did not. For 1 df, this gives a Chi Square of 40·76, which is significant at the 0·0000000001% level of confidence—roughly.

The same procedure can be carried out for Classes 3 and 1 in respect of Class 2. Of those who fell into Class 3, 124 (or 88%) fell also into Class 2 and 17 (or 12%) did not. Of those who fell into Class 1 (other than Class 3s) 153 (or 66%) fell into Class 2 and 80 (or 34%) did not. For 1 df, this gives a Chi Square of 22·70, which is significant at least at the 0·1% level of confidence.

When discussing Neurotic Symptoms and Dysthymic States in the previous chapter, it was predicted that the former class would be commoner among day-patients and in-patients than would Dysthymic States; whereas the Dysthymic State class would be commoner than the Neurotic Symptoms class among normals and out-patients. The first prediction was correct for all four groups. The Neurotic Symptoms class was commoner than the Dysthymic States class for both male and female in-patients and day-patients. The prediction was wrong for both male and female out-patients and just so for young female normals.

The contention that among patients an inclusive, non-reflexive, relationship exists between the classes of personal illness is supported by the fact that, in virtually all cases where membership of a class is established, the person also belongs to all the lower classes and the converse is seen not to hold, i.e. the model is uni-directional.

The next stage of the investigation was to try to determine whether or not the hierarchy is maintained during the course of remission of symptoms. The 68 patients, who were re-examined after approximately one month, were all in-patients. About two-thirds of these were an almost complete sample from one Canadian hospital. The remaining third from one Scottish hospital were a much less complete sample; but no deliberate selection was involved. The results are shown in Table 3.

Ignoring "Other patterns", cases:
    above the solid line have "moved down" at re-test (n = 38);
    below the dotted line have "moved up" at re-test (n = 6);
    between the two lines maintain the same hierarchy class (n = 16).

TABLE 3
DSSI class change after one month

Class	Test Pattern	Other	Re-test Normal 0000	DS 0001	NS 0011	ID 0111	DD 1111	Totals	%
DD	1111	1	—	2	—	1	1	5	7·4
ID	0111	1	—	3	5	1	1	11	16·2
NS	0011	1	6	9	1	3	—	20	29·4
DS	0001	—	12	6	1	1	—	20	29·4
Normal	0000	—	7	—	—	—	—	7	10·3
Other patterns		3	—	2	—	—	—	5	7·4
Totals		6	25	22	7	6	2	68	
%		8·8	36·8	32·4	10·3	8·8	2·9		

On first testing, five patients (or 7·4%) did not conform to the hierarchy. This figure is almost identical with that found for the 253 inpatients of which the present 68 are a part. In terms of highest class membership the present group differs in containing a clear excess of Dysthymic States and a slight under-representation of Integrated Delusions. On second testing, six patients did not conform to the hierarchy (i.e. 8·8%). Although it is evident that the patients as a group changed markedly, they have not departed from the hierarchy.

Of 63 who fitted the hierarchy on first testing, three ceased to do so on re-testing; but, of the five who did not fit on first testing, two did so on re-testing. Leaving aside non-fitting cases on *either* occasion, 38 improved, 16 remained the same (of whom seven could not improve, having started in Class 0, i.e. the non-personally ill) and six were worse. Thus, 72% of those who could improve did so; but only 34% claimed to be symptom-free.

Of the 68 forming the total group only 37% scored as non-personally ill at one month re-test, despite the earlier mentioned excess of Dysthymic States. It is perhaps worth commenting that of the people initially scoring as non-personally ill some may be chronic patients, alcoholics or personality deviants. On the other hand, a total symptom score (i.e. ignoring cut-off points) would probably differentiate some of them from non-patient subjects.

Of the 44 fitting cases who change class 73% do so by one class only, i.e. 27 of 38 who improve and five of the six who get worse.

DISCUSSION

There was reasonable agreement among psychiatrists and clinical psychologists that the items of the Delusions-Symptoms-States Inventory had been "correctly" allocated to their predicted clinical syndromes, with the exception of state of Depression items. These were almost all allocated by psychiatrists, but not by psychologists, to Psychotic Depression. Whilst noting this disagreement, we still feel justified in abiding by our original formulations.

The responses of subjects to the items of the DSSI conformed to a very considerable extent to the hierarchy of classes of personal illness. This applied whether the subjects were male or female, in-patients, day-patients, out-patients or normals. Those who affirmed Delusions of Disintegration also affirmed Integrated Delusions, Neurotic Symptoms and Dysthymic States; those who affirmed Integrated Delusions also affirmed Neurotic Symptoms and Dysthymic States; those who affirmed Neurotic Symptoms also affirmed Dysthymic States. The converse did not hold. There was, therefore, considerable support for the notion that the relationship between classes of personal illness is inclusive and non-reflexive.

It has been objected that it would be perfectly easy to write items in such a way as to maximize the likelihood of obtaining a hierarchy. This certainly was not done deliberately; nor do we consider that it would be easy. This objection must presumably mean that items should, to maximize the chances of obtaining a hierarchy, become more generalized as one moved down the hierarchy. From our inspection this does not seem to hold. Seriously to advance this view it would be necessary to establish that a group of psychiatrists could agree in rating all the items for degree of generality. This seemed to us so improbable that the exercise has not been carried out. Anyone wishing to do so would, of course, be supplied with the full list of items. Finally, the vast majority of items have been found acceptable by 25 independent judges for the purpose for which they were originally intended.

At re-test in-patients fit the hierarchy to the same degree that they, and a much larger sample of mixed psychiatric patients, did at initial testing. These results indicate that either the symptoms further up the hierarchy remit before those lower in the hierarchy or they remit together. Without sequential testing, say weekly, a definitive answer is impossible. It is clear, however, that the symptoms lower in the hierarchy do not remit first. This is much less surprising than may appear at first sight. It is true that a state of Anxiety would generally be regarded as more amenable to treatment than, say, Compulsive symptoms or than delusions of Persecution; but this judgment is based on cases diagnosed respectively as Anxiety State, Obsessional Neurosis and Paranoid Psychosis, i.e. these diagnoses basically give affirmative information on only one syndrome. Within the hierarchy, however, we may be considering, for example, an Obsessional Compulsive (a Class 2 set) who also has a state of Anxiety (a Class 1 set). If the anxiety went first, we would be left with an obsessional compulsive neurotic who was not anxious. This seems less likely—except perhaps in the case of a leucotomized subject—than some anxiety outlasting the obsessional symptoms.

The fact that patients tend to move down the hierarchy during the course of recovery is not easy to accommodate within disease entity models as opposed to other medical models. Thus, a schizophrenic may be treated with phenothiazines and then assessed as very much improved, improved or unimproved. As we mentioned in the previous chapter, complete acceptance of a disease entity model logically entails that "improved" refer to the symptoms of schizophrenia alone. Fortunately even the diminishing number of staunch supporters of disease entity models are probably somewhat inconsistent in that their practice may often be at odds with theory.

In the present hierarchy terms, it may be that "very much improved" would refer to those patients who had moved down to Class 0, the symptom-free; "somewhat improved" to those who had moved down to Class 2 or 1. A study designed to investigate these assumptions might be of interest and value.

Again, strictly according to a disease entity model, the patient who has moved down from Class 3 to Class 2 should be given another course of ECT or whatever; but, according to the hierarchy model, the phobic symptoms, or whatever remained, should be treated by the method which the clinician thought most appropriate for that condition (e.g. behaviour therapy). It might be justifiable to carry out a study designed to compare the results of working strictly according to the disease entity or to the hierarchy model.

Summary

The Delusions-Symptoms-States Inventory (DSSI-R) has been described with its 12 sets of 7 items each, corresponding to Delusions of Disintegration (Class 4); Integrated Delusions (Class 3)—delusions of Persecution, of Grandeur and of Contrition; Neurotic Symptoms (Class 2)—Conversion, Dissociative, Phobic, Compulsive and Ruminative symptoms; and Dysthymic States (Class 1)—states of Anxiety, of Depression and of Elation.

Patients scoring four or more on any set were allocated to the class within which the set fell. The final "diagnosis" was the highest class entered.

Ten groups were examined: male and female in-patients, day-patients and out-patients, normals over 21 years of age and normals under 22 years of age. More than 90% of all groups conformed to the hierarchy. It would seem that "Where the greater malady is fix'd, the lesser" is felt; but it is often not noticed.

Results indicate that the hierarchy is maintained after a period of one month, even though there has been a considerable reduction in the symptoms of the group as a whole. One can at least conclude from this that, when associated with a greater malady, the lesser malady does not remit first. Either the greater malady remits first or they remit together.

The fact that roughly one third of patients who originally reported symptoms did not do so after one month, perhaps suggests that for them treatment ought to proceed within the universe of discourse of personality traits and attitudes. That most patients retain some symptoms, often having "moved down" one hierarchy class level, should direct attention to the use of combined or consecutive treatments in conjunction with continuous assessments.

Appendix A

The following state of Depression items were allocated by a majority of judges to Psychotic Depression:

sD 7.   Recently the future has seemed hopeless.

sD 19.   Recently I have lost interest in just about *everything*.

sD 31.   Recently I have been so depressed that I have thought of doing away with myself.

sD 55. Recently I have been so low in spirits that I have sat for ages doing absolutely nothing.

sD 67. Recently I have been depressed without knowing why.

sD 79. Recently I have gone to bed not caring if I never woke up.

The following state of Elation (or Hypomania) items were allocated to Mania:

sE 28. Recently new ideas and schemes have been *rushing* through my head one after another.

sE 40. Recently I have had so much pep and energy that I could hardly stop doing things.

sE 64. Recently I have been so cheerful that I have wanted to decorate myself with *much* brighter, *more* colourful things than I usually do.

The following Conversion item was allocated to Anxiety State:

CVs 50. Recently I have been unable to control my violent shaking.

The first two Dissociative items were allocated to Schizophrenia and the third to Conversion Hysteria:

Ds 48. Recently people around me have seemed strange, unfamiliar, or different.

Ds 60. Recently things around me have seemed odd, unfamiliar, or changed.

Ds 72. Recently I have lost consciousness for a few seconds without actually falling.

The following Phobic items were allocated to Ruminative Obsessional:

Ps 32. Recently I have been afraid of handling some weapon or sharp object.

Ps 44. Recently I have had an *unreasonable* fear of germs.

The following delusions of Grandeur (or Manic) items were allocated to Schizophrenia:

dG 33. Recently I have felt that I have been sent to save the world.

dG 81. Recently I have felt that I have special, almost magical, powers.

6

Groups Within the Classes of Personal Illness

Introduction

One of the reasons for the current wave of opposition to diagnosis in psychiatry is the alleged overlap of syndromes. This argument is based very largely on clinical impressions and is deficient in empirical support. The aim of this chapter is to try to ascertain to what extent the claim is justified when one does and when one does not utilize the hierarchy of classes of personal illness and when one does and does not include anxiety and depressive states within the Neurosis class.

We have taken the view that states of Anxiety and of Depression should not be included within the Neurosis class, principally because neurotic symptoms are inclusive of dysthymic states, whereas dysthymic states are not inclusive of neurotic symptoms. They do not, therefore, belong at the same diagnostic level.

We have followed Henderson and Gillespie (1946) in distinguishing between the two obsessional conditions of compulsions and ruminations.

> Where constant pre-occupation occurs with a single topic, itself usually of apparently minor importance (e.g. an anxious preoccupation with the idea of dirt) against the patient's better judgment and to his distress, *"obsessive-ruminative"* state is a fair description. *"Obsessive-compulsive"* state is applied to a similar condition in which the preoccupation issues in motor acts of an apparently trifling or meaningless kind.

We have followed Cameron (1963) in distinguishing between conversion and dissociative reactions. "The defensive measures used in dissociative reactions are those of *over-exclusion, denial* and *repression,* which relate them to conversion reactions, and those of *ego-splitting* and *isolation*, which relate them to obsessive compulsive reactions."

We wish, therefore, to deal with: (1) the frequency of unmixed syndromes within each patient's *highest* class in the hierarchy; (2) the frequency of mixed syndromes in those cases in which the diagnosis lies between any pair of syndromes within the highest class; (3) the frequency of unmixed syndromes within each patient's *lower* classes in the hierarchy; (4) the frequency with which the 480 patients scored four or more on each of the 12 sets of the Delusions-Symptoms-States Inventory (DSSI), regardless of their final "diagnosis" or class allocation; and (5) the relationship between each possible pair of sets, again ignoring final class allocation.

Results

Since Class 4 (Disintegrated Delusions) includes only one group, the concept of unmixed syndromes is inapplicable. The earlier suggestion that groups might be formed by considering whether or not they had the Class 3 delusions of Grandeur, Persecution, or Contrition is a departure from the method used for the other classes and cannot, therefore, be used here.

WITHIN CLASS 3—INTEGRATED DELUSIONS

Any subject who does not score more than three for delusions of Disintegration and who does score four or more on any of the sets of Class 3 is classified within that class, no matter what he may score on the sets of Classes 1 or 2.

Table 4 shows the number of patients who fall into one group only or into two or more groups within Class 3.

TABLE 4

Assignment of Integrated Psychotics to groups within that class (Class 3)

Patients	n	dP	dG	dC	dP/dG	dP/dC	dG/dC	All 3	% unmixed
Out	118	4	1	14	0	2	1	0	86
Day	109	1	2	12	0	0	1	0	94
In	253	12	7	34	0	14	4	1	74
Total	480	17	10	60	0	16	6	1	79

As would be expected, delusions of Contrition were much the most common and delusions of Contrition and of Persecution occurred more often together than did other combinations. Approximately four out of every five cases fell into one group only. The claim that there is a large overlap between syndromes does not apply to Class 3 patients.

We now wish to look at the frequency of mixed syndromes in those cases in which the diagnosis clearly lies between each pair of syndromes within Class 3. The results are shown in Table 5.

TABLE 5

The frequency of mixed syndromes where the diagnosis lies between any
pair of syndromes within Class 3

dP 63% (17);	dG 37% (10);	mixed 0%
dP 18% (17);	dC 65% (60);	mixed 17% (16)
dG 13% (10);	dC 79% (60);	mixed 8% (6)

Delusions of Persecution are as likely to be found together with delusions of Contrition as alone. This is somewhat less true of delusions of Grandeur. That they should ever occur together might be surprising were it not that the time span of the DSSI would allow for someone having swung from one to the other within the recent past. It was noted that this did in fact occur between first testing and subsequent testing one month later.

WITHIN CLASS 2—NEUROTIC SYMPTOMS

Any subject who does not score more than three on delusions of Disintegration or on any of the Class 3 sets, but who does score four or more on any of the sets within Class 2 is classified as a Class 2 patient, no matter what he may score on the sets of Class 1.

Table 6 shows the number of patients who fall into one group only or into two or more groups within Class 2.

Despite there being five groups, almost half the patients fall into one group only. Phobic patients constitute the largest group, followed by Ruminatives.

We now turn to the frequency of mixed syndromes in those cases in which the diagnosis lies between pairs of syndromes within Class 2. The results are shown in Table 7.

Conversion and dissociative symptoms seldom occur together with any one of the remaining groups or with each other. This lends some

TABLE 6

Assignment of Neurotics to groups within that class (Class 2)

Patients	n	CV	D	P	CP	R	CV/D	CV/P	CV/CP	CV/R	D/P	D/CP	D/R	P/CP	P/R	CP/R	>2	% unmixed
Out	118	0	1	10	6	5	0	1	0	1	0	0	0	1	4	4	14	47
Day	109	3	0	12	3	8	0	3	0	0	0	0	0	4	3	3	14	49
In	253	6	4	11	4	10	1	1	0	0	2	1	2	4	2	5	20	48
Total	480	9	5	33	13	23	1	5	0	1	2	1	2	9	9	12	48	48

TABLE 7

The frequency of mixed syndromes where the diagnosis lies between any
pair of syndromes within Class 2

CVs 60% (9);	Ds 33% (5);	mixed 7% (1).
CVs 19% (9);	Ps 70% (33);	mixed 11% (5).
CVs 41% (9);	CPs 59% (13);	mixed 0%.
CVs 27% (9);	Rs 70% (23);	mixed 3% (1).
CPs 27% (13);	Rs 48% (23);	mixed 25% (9).
Ds 12% (5);	Ps 82% (33);	mixed 5% (2).
Ds 26% (5);	CPs 68% (13);	mixed 5% (1).
Ds 17% (5);	Rs 77% (23);	mixed 7% (2).
Ps 60% (33);	CPs 24% (13);	mixed 16% (9).
Ps 51% (33);	Rs 35% (23);	mixed 14% (12).

support to Cameron's (*op. cit.*) distinction between conversion and dissociative symptoms. However, his claimed similarity in some respects
between dissociative symptoms and compulsive symptoms does not seem
to be borne out. He was, however, referring to underlying mechanisms
rather than to symptoms. Even though the mixture of ruminative and
compulsive symptoms is the highest of any pair, it still leaves room for
a viable distinction, in accordance with the views of Henderson and
Gillespie (1946).

WITHIN CLASS 1—DYSTHYMIC STATES

Any subject who does not score more than three on any set within
Classes 4, 3 or 2, but who does score four or more on any set within
Class 1 is classified as a Class 1 patient.

Table 8 shows the number of patients who fall into one group only
or into two or more groups within Class 1.

TABLE 8

Assignment of Dysthymic States to groups within that class (Class 1)

Patients	n	sA	sD	sE	sA/sD	sA/sE	sD/sE	All 3	% unmixed
Out	118	5	10	2	9	0	0	1	63
Day	109	2	1	1	12	0	0	1	24
In	253	10	10	3	17	1	0	0	56
Total	480	17	21	6	38	1	0	2	52

Just over half the patients fall within one class only, despite the fact
that, as Goldberg (1973) has suggested, Anxiety and Depressive states

are not readily distinguishable. In this study this applies particularly to day-patients. For this finding we have no explanation.

Once again we turn to the frequency of mixed syndromes in those cases in which the diagnosis lies between pairs of syndromes. Here, as elsewhere, this constitutes a minority of cases. The results are shown in Table 9.

TABLE 9

The frequency of mixed syndromes where the diagnosis lies between any pair of syndromes within Class 1

sA 22% (17);	sD 28% (21);	mixed 50% (38).
sA 71% (17);	sE 25% (6);	mixed 4% (1).
sD 78% (21);	sE 22% (6);	mixed 0%.

Of all pairs of syndromes within their respective classes, states of Anxiety and of Depression show much the highest admixture. Even though 50% of these cases are mixed, the number who fall into one of these syndromes only is perhaps sufficiently substantial to warrant retention of the distinction until more data are available on, for example, personality characteristics, outcome, etc.

Of the 480 patients who were examined, 112 fell into either Class 4 or Class 0 (the non-personally ill) and could not, therefore, be considered here. Of the remaining 368 who fell into Classes 1, 2 or 3, 214 (or 58%) fell into one group only within the class to which they were assigned. This, therefore, is the overall situation when the hierarchy of classes of personal illness is used, in which any syndrome in a higher class takes precedence over any syndrome in a lower class. When the hierarchy is not used, the percentage of cases showing an unmixed syndrome falls from 58% to 13%.

Traditionally states of Anxiety and of Depression are included within the Neurotic Class. It is desirable, therefore, to show the effect of so including them. Since states of Elation are not usually included among the Neuroses, they will likewise be excluded here. Thus, instead of our Classes 1 and 2, we now have a Neurotic Class made up of seven groups—the present five plus states of Anxiety and states of Depression.

Out of the 256 subjects who fell into at least one of these groups, 205 fell into two or more groups and only 51 into a single group. On this basis, only 20% can be described as unmixed syndromes. It is clear that it is the states of Anxiety and of Depression who are the tinted folk in the woodpile. As we argued earlier, they do not belong at the same level of classification. One cannot, for example, say that all phobics are compulsives. In fact, only 26% are (see Table 6). Nor can one say that all compulsives are phobics. In fact only 16% are. One cannot even say that all Anxiety states are Depressive states. In fact, only 66% are (see Table 7). Nor can one say that all Depressive states are Anxiety states. In fact, only 65% are. One can, on the other hand, say that all, or virtually all, Phobics are Anxiety states. In fact, 95% are. But one cannot say that all Anxiety states are Phobics. In fact, only 44% are. To reiterate, between group within-class relationships are of an either and/or type; those between classes are inclusive and non-reflexive.

We now turn to our third question with regard to the frequency of unmixed syndromes within each patient's lower classes in the hierarchy. Do unmixed syndromes within a particular class occur with the same frequency among those who are and those who are not classifiable in any higher class?

Table 10 shows the assignment of members of Class 4 (Delusions of Disintegration) and of Class 3 (Integrated Delusions) to groups within Class 3.

TABLE 10

Assignment of members of Class 4 and of Class 3 to groups within Class 3
(Integrated Delusions)

Class	dP	dG	dC	mixed	% unmixed
4	2	2	6	32	24
3	15	9	60	23	79

Unmixed syndromes within Class 3 occurred significantly less often in those with Delusions of Disintegration (for df $= 1$, Chi Squared $= 32\cdot00$; p $< 0\cdot001$) than in members of Class 3. Thus, those with Delusions of Disintegration are much more likely to have more than one type of integrated delusion.

Table 11 shows the assignment of members of Classes 4, 3 and 2 to groups within Class 2 (Neurotic Symptoms).

Unmixed syndromes within Class 2 occurred significantly less often in those with Integrated Delusions (for df $= 1$, Chi Squared $= 11\cdot16$; p $< 0\cdot001$) than in members of Class 2. Likewise, unmixed syndromes within Class 2 occurred significantly less often in those with Delusions

TABLE 11

Assignment of members of Classes 4, 3 and 2 to groups within Class 2
(Neurotic Symptoms)

Class	CVs	Ds	Ps	CPs	Rs	Mixed	% unmixed
4	0	0	0	0	1	39	2½
3	2	4	3	7	9	68	27
2	9	5	33	13	23	90	48

of Disintegration (for df $= 1$, Chi Squared $= 28·14$; p $< 0·001$) than
in members of Class 2.

Table 12 shows the assignment of members of Classes 4, 3, 2 and 1 to
groups within Class 1 (Dysthymic States).

TABLE 12

Assignment of members of Classes 4, 3, 2 and 1 to groups within Class 1
(Dysthymic States)

Class	sA	sD	sE	Mixed	% unmixed
4	1	3	0	37	10
3	2	5	2	93	9
2	16	6	1	109	17
1	17	21	6	41	52

Unmixed syndromes within Class 1 occur significantly less often in
those with Neurotic Symptoms (for df $= 1$, Chi Squared $= 28·57$; p
$< 0·001$); in those with Integrated Delusions (Chi Squared $= 42·09$;
p $< 0·001$); in those with Delusions of Disintegration (Chi Squared $=$
$20·70$; p $< 0·001$) than in members of Class 1.

We have now to take up the question of the frequency with which
the 480 patients scored four or more on each of the 12 sets of the DSSI,
regardless of the final class allocation.

Table 13 shows the number and percentage of patients scoring four
or more on each set.

States of Anxiety and of Depression were much the most frequently
endorsed. Although the hierarchy was intended to apply only to classes,
it seems reasonably applicable to groups between classes. Only the state
of Elation and delusions of Grandeur and of Contrition are somewhat
misplaced.

TABLE 13

The number and percentage of patients falling into each group, regardless of final DSSI "diagnosis"

Class	Group	n	%
1	State of Anxiety (sA)	342	71
1	State of Depression (sD)	331	69
2	Ruminative symptoms (Rs)	197	41
2	Phobic symptoms (Ps)	181	38
2	Compulsive symptoms (Cs)	155	32
3	Delusions of Contrition (dC)	118	24
2	Dissociative symptoms (Ds)	104	21
1	State of Elation (sE)	103	21
2	Conversion symptoms (CVs)	95	20
3	Delusions of Persecution (dP)	61	13
4	Delusions of Disintegration (dD)	47	10
3	Delusions of Grandeur (dG)	42	9

Table 14 shows the percentage of patients falling into at least one of each pair of groups who fall into both. The five highest and the five lowest percentages only are shown.

TABLE 14

Percentage of patients falling into at least one of each pair of groups who fall into both (the five highest and the five lowest percentages only)

Classes	Groups	% mixed	Classes	Groups	% mixed
1	sA/sD	73	3 & 2	dG/Ps	12
2 & 1	Rs/sA	51	4 & 1	dD/sD	12
2	CP/Rs	48	4 & 1	dD/sA	11
2 & 1	Rs/sD	48	3 & 1	dG/sD	9
2 & 1	Ps/sA	48	3 & 1	dG/sA	8

In more than one-third of the between-group between-class comparisons the percentage of mixed cases falls below any of the between-group within-class comparisons.

Within Class 1, the highest mixture is between states of Anxiety and of Depression (73%); the lowest is between states of Depression and of Elation (21%). Within Class 2, the highest mixture is between Compulsive and Ruminative symptoms (48%) and the lowest between Compulsive and Conversion symptoms (28%). Within Class 3, the highest is between delusions of Persecution and of Contrition (29%) and the lowest between delusions of Contrition and of Grandeur (20%). On clinical grounds it would be difficult to conceive of a more predictable result.

Table 15 shows, of those falling into each of the 12 groups, the percentage in each instance who fall into the remaining groups.

TABLE 15

Of those falling into each group, the percentage who fall into each of the remaining groups

Of those scoring 4 or more on:					Percentage who score 4 or more on:								
n	Group	sE	sD	sA	Rs	CPs	Ps	Ds	CVs	dC	dG	dP	dD
47	dD	38	83	85	91+	77+	68	70+	47+	72+	53+	57+	
61	dP	36	85	80	74	62	62	52	34	66	30		44
42	dG	60+	71−	71−	76	67	57	64	43	64		43	60+
118	dC	31	95+	92	80	58	61	60	40		23	34	29
95	CVs	34	89	93+	73	58	69+	47		49	19	22	23
104	Ds	38	87	92	74	62	65		43	57	26	32	32
181	Ps	31	88	93+	64	50		37	36	40	13	21	18
155	CPs	35	88	90	74		58	42	35	45	18	25	23
197	Rs	32	87	93+		58	59	39	35	48	16	23	22
342	sA	25	83		54	41−	49	28	26−	32−	9−	14−	12−
331	sD	23−		86	52−	41−	48−	27−	26−	34	9−	16	12−
103	sE		74	83	62	53	54	39	31	35	24	21	17

Reading columns

A + has been given for the highest percentage in each column and a − for the lowest percentage in each column. It can be seen that the group *most* likely to come up on delusions of Disintegration is the delusions of Grandeur group (60%); the groups *least* likely to come up on delusions of Disintegration are the states of Anxiety and of Depression (12%). The group *most* likely to come up on delusions of Persecution is the delusions of Disintegration group (57%); the group *least* likely to come up on delusions of Persecution is the state of Anxiety group (14%) and so on.

In the 50 instances in which pairs from different classes are compared there are only eight in which the frequency is greater in the lower class. This is further evidence that the hierarchy of classes applies tolerably well to groups *between* classes, though not, of course, *within* classes.

Reading rows

Those scoring 4+ on: dD. dP. dG. dC. CVs. Ds. Ps. CPs. Rs. sA. sD. sE.
Most likely to be 4+ on: Rs. sD. Rs.   sD. sA.   sA. sA. sA.   sA. sD. sA. sA.
Least likely to be 4+ on: sE. dG. CVs. dG. dG.   dG. dG. dG. dG. dG. dG. dD.

As one might expect from Table 13, the "Most likely row" is dominated by sA and the "Least likely row" by dG. It is of interest that the Dissociative group is consistently the most likely of the non-psychotic groups to come up on delusions of all types. As Cameron (*op. cit.*) has noted: "Often a dissociative reaction borders upon the psychotic". He does, however, point out that "the dissociative patient usually does not need restitutive processes, such as the delusions and hallucinations".

Discussion and conclusions

The results indicate that 58% of 480 psychiatric patients fell into only one syndrome within the class to which they were finally assigned, when the hierarchy of classes of personal illness was used; when the hierarchy was not used, the percentage of unmixed syndromes fell to a mere 13%. It is, therefore, quite clear that, if the hierarchy of classes of personal illness is completely ignored, the argument that psychiatric diagnosis is of no value because there is too much overlap between syndromes is strongly supported.

We have noted that Bleuler (*op. cit.*) claimed that all the symptoms of manic-depressive psychosis may occur in schizophrenia. Without some hierarchical notion, how does one decide which of the clusters of symptoms is so dominant as to warrant making one diagnosis rather than the other? There are no public rules. Each clinician is left to his own subjective devices. The degree of subjectivity is extreme in such diagnoses as "latent depression". Hill (*op. cit.*) has said, "A clear distinction must be made between circumstances in which depression has developed and circumstances in which, given understanding of the patient's situation, it might have been expected but has not occurred. In the latter circumstances we commonly observe those first-line defensive neurotic postures, such as . . . hysterical or obsessional symptom formation", among many others. He goes on to say, "this distinction is important if only because antidepressant drugs and ECT are of little therapeutic value in cases where depression has not occurred but has been defended against". Hill does not state what his diagnosis would be in such cases; but there is little doubt that some clinicians would diagnose "latent depression"; whereas others would diagnose "obsessional neurosis", or whatever. Some would argue that there are no obsessional symptoms which are not defences against depression or anxiety. On this view, all cases could be diagnosed as "latent depression", in which case the diagnosis is uninformative. If it is held that there are some obsessional symptoms which are not defences against depression, how are they to be distinguished from those which are? Responses to antidepressant drugs or ECT do not serve. What does? We are not aware that any differentiae have been set forth.

If the hierarchical principle is used sporadically, as appears to be the current practice, this must militate against high inter-judge reliability of diagnosis. If the hierarchy is used systematically, the results are not discouraging, particularly when states of Anxiety and of Depression are taken out of the Neurotic Class and put into a separate Dysthymic States Class. Then about half of the Neurotics and of the Dysthymic States have unmixed syndromes; when they are included in the Neurotic Class, the percentage falls to 20.

Unmixed syndromes within any particular class occur significantly more often in those who are not classifiable in any higher class. Thus, when the Dysthymic States of those with delusions of Disintegration are considered, a mere 10% fall into only one of those Dysthymic States; on the other hand, 52% of those classifiable as Dysthymic States fall into one such group only. It appears, therefore, that, as the illness becomes increasingly severe, symptoms become more and more heterogeneous, incorporating more and more of the symptoms characteristic of the classes lower in the hierarchy. This is in accord with the view expressed by Gruenberg (*op. cit.*) and cited in Chapter 4, that precedence is given to those conditions which have the more varied manifestations. All this suggests that more and more troops are brought up to try to hold the line; but if it still breaks, the destruction may well be the greater.

Since then it can be said that those who fall into Classes 4, 3 or 2 tend to have mixed syndromes in any class lower than their own, the question was raised as to whether members of a particular class who fell into more than one group within that class are more likely than those who fall into one group only to move into a higher class in the hierarchy. Thus, for example, is a neurotic who manifests ruminative, compulsive and phobic symptoms more likely than one who manifests only ruminative symptoms to develop a psychotic depression? This requires a follow-up period of some years; but the problem is researchable and does perhaps deserve investigation, since it might enable one, for example, to predict schizophrenia at a very early stage. The not too serious rule of thumb generalization was that, if a patient appeared to have everything except schizophrenic symptoms, he was probably about to become schizophrenic; if he appeared to have everything, including schizophrenic symptoms, but you didn't believe it, he was probably a psychopath. The first proposition at least may have considerable justification.

When the hierarchy was ignored and consideration was given simply to the percentage of As who were Bs and the percentage of Bs who were As etc., it was found that patients complained more often of delusions of Contrition than they did of Conversion or Dissociative symptoms or states of Elation; fewer patients complained of a state of Elation than complained of Phobic, Compulsive or Ruminative symptoms and complaints of delusions of Disintegration were marginally less than delusions of Grandeur. Although the hierarchy was intended to apply only to classes, it does seem that it applies to groups between classes as well. It does not, of course, apply to groups within classes. It is logically necessary that the relationship between groups within classes be of an either and/or type.

The argument that psychiatric diagnosis is of no value because overlapping syndromes are so much the rule does not appear to be sustainable within the framework of the hierarchy of classes of personal illness.

7

The DSSI Personal Disturbance Scale

Introduction

There is general agreement that short symptom scales are useful in evaluating treatments (Kellner, 1971, 1972; Shapiro, 1961) and for screening out the psychiatrically disturbed in the general population (Goldberg, 1972, Kapur *et al.*, 1974, Wing *et al.*, 1974). Several instruments exist for these purposes; but they differ in their form, content, breadth etc. In order that the current scale may be evaluated it is necessary, therefore, to show how it fits within this spectrum. In this connection there are four main points to be made.

1. Enquiry is made only of current psychiatric state. No reference is made to past psychiatric (or other medical) illnesses and the respondent is not asked how he *usually* feels, thinks or behaves. This latter type of information can be invaluable in some contexts; but we believe that it should be gathered separately. Insistence on present state alone should render the instrument more sensitive to change.

2. Following from this, a deliberate attempt was made to exclude personality attitudinal or "predisposition" items. Some scales, such as the Middlesex Hospital Questionnaire (Crown and Crisp), although predominantly symptomatological, includes a section named "hysterical *personality*". A far more extreme, and converse, position is seen in the common use of putative stable personality measures for the assessment of symptom change. The difficulties which this procedure raises have been considered by Coppen and Metcalfe (1965) and by Kendell and Discipio (1968). The former concluded that "changes in clinical state can profoundly alter a subject's scores on the MPI" and the latter state that "unless the standard instructions are amended depressed patients

obtain misleading scores on the EPI . . . this is because, to a considerable extent, they rate their current state of mind rather than their normal selves." Although there is no absolute sense in which a symptom versus attitude dichotomy can be made, guidelines have been suggested in Chapter 3 and elsewhere.

3. In common with several other measures produced by psychologists, in contrast to psychiatrists, report is by self-rating. The choice of response is not, however, just of a yes/no type, but includes gradations within positive answers. In the present instance this entails deciding whether the presence of the state causes a little, a lot or almost unbearable distress.

4. Finally, the most distinctive feature of the scale is that it is derived empirically from the whole Delusions-Symptoms-States Inventory and logically from the hierarchy of classes of personal illness.

It has been suggested that it might prove useful to think in terms of four classes of personal illness. These classes were: Class 4 (Delusions of Disintegration); Class 3 (Integrated Delusions); Class 2 (Neurotic Symptoms); Class 1 (Dysthymic States). It was argued, and demonstrated with data from the DSSI, that virtually all members of Class 4 were also members of Classes 3, 2 and 1; that virtually all members of Class 3 were also members of Classes 2 and 1; and that virtually all members of Class 2 were also members of Class 1. A scale based solely on Class 1 should, therefore, prove an economical and efficient instrument for identifying the personally disturbed, i.e. members of Classes 4, 3, 2 and 1.

Score distributions on all the sets of the DSSI for normal subjects and for patients should serve to underline this point. These are shown in Table 16.

TABLE 16

Score distributions for 136 normals and 480 patients on the 12 sets of the DSSI (percentages)

Score	sA		sD		sE		CVs		Ds		Ps		CPs		Rs	
	N	P	N	P	N	P	N	P	N	P	N	P	N	P	N	P
0	54	7	77	11	59	41	90	42	96	50	57	26	85	30	69	30
1	26	6	9	8	8	8	7	13	1	10	27	12	10	15	19	11
2	12	8	4	7	17	19	2	16	1	11	11	14	4	13	7	11
3	2	7	5	4	4	11	1	9	1	8	2	10	1	10	2	7
4	2	6	1	5	6	5		5		5	1	8		12		10
5	1	6	1	5	2	5		5		5	1	8		5	1	5
6	1	6	1	5	1	5		3		4		5		6	1	6
7	1	6		6		1		2		3		5		4		6
8		8	1	5	1	2		1		2		3		2		4
9		7		5				1		1		3		1		3

TABLE 16 – *contd.*

Score	sA N	sA P	sD N	sD P	sE N	sE P	CVs N	CVs P	Ds N	Ds P	Ps N	Ps P	CPs N	CPs P	Rs N	Rs P
10		7	1	5	1	1		1						1		3
11		6		6	1	1				1		1				2
12		5		7	1	1		1		1		1				1
13		4		5												1
14		4		4								1				
15		3		3		1										1
16		2		2												
17		1		2												
18				1												
19				2												
20				1												
21				1												

Score	dP N	dP P	dG N	dG P	dC N	dC P	dD N	dD P
0	98	73	90	77	97	50	97	66
1	1	5	4	5	2	8	2	8
2		4	4	6		10	1	9
3		5	1	4	1	7		7
4		2	1	2		4		1
5		2	1	1		3		1
6		2		1		3		1
7	1	1		1		3		1
8		1		1		2		1
9				1		2		1
10		1				2		
11		1				1		
12		1				1		
13						1		
14								1
15 to 21								

	Normals			Patients		
	Kurtosis	Skewness	Median	Kurtosis	Skewness	Median
sA	6·07	2·26	0·0	−0·75	0·23	7·02
sD	13·55	3·41	0·0	−0·88	0·30	7·23
sE	7·96	2·58	0·0	4·63	2·01	1·55
CVs	16·48	3·91	0·0	4·28	1·89	1·12
Ds	38·59	6·10	0·0	3·35	1·77	0·54
Ps	3·88	1·82	0·0	0·99	1·14	2·34
CPs	8·97	2·99	0·0	3·91	1·59	1·86
Rs	9·65	2·84	0·0	0·46	1·05	2·37
dP	125·73	11·22	0·0	11·04	3·16	0·0
dG	38·99	5·73	0·0	16·78	3·79	0·0
dC	74·86	8·25	0·0	3·16	1·83	0·0
dD	48·05	6·71	0·0	11·66	3·07	0·0

It is clear that normals and patients differ very greatly on all measures, except possibly for the special case of state of Elation. All the normal group's distributions are exceedingly skewed, as are those of patients, with the possible exception of state of Anxiety and state of Depression, both of which are platykurtic. Since the great majority of patients score abnormally on state of Anxiety and on state of Depression, a combination of these two scales is likely to provide an economical and efficient measure of Personal Disturbance for use as a screening device.

DSSI Class 1 (Dysthymic States) consists of three groups—states of Anxiety, of Depression and of Elation. There are three sets of seven items each, which are intended to assess the presence of these dysthmic states. The present scale consists only of the seven sA and seven sD items and can, therefore, be referred to as the DSSI/sAD Scale. The state of Elation items have been omitted, as they seem, as we have already indicated, to be a uniquely different case from all other DSSI sets.

Limitations of the sAD scale

Goldberg (1972, *op. cit.*), in discussing his "General Health Questionnaire", stated that the questionnaire "missed chronic schizophrenics, organics, and hypomanics", whilst including too many young normals as "false positives". With slight reservations only we believe that the DSSI/sAD would be expected to have closely similar limitations.

Some young normals, for example, may claim to have a depressed mood, but may be distinguishable from the more pathologically depressed in lacking the other seemingly necessary facet of depression—the catastrophically lowered self-esteem to which reference has already been made. Data of our own, gathered on 98 normals with a modal age of 19 years, give a higher mean score than adults and a greater percentage exceeding the anxiety and depression cutting points. In coining the phrase "Catcher in the Rye" syndrome, Fish (1962) highlighted the psychiatric aspects and frequency of adolescent identity crises—"It is usually a reactive unhappiness rather than a true depressive illness." That the highest incidence of parasuicide occurs in the 15–25 age range (Aitken, *et al.*, 1969) might, however, caution us against an overconfident assumption that positive responses in the young are "false".

With regard to chronic schizophrenics, Priest (1973) found that "On the PI Scale" (of the Symptom-Sign Inventory) "28% of chronic schizophrenics obtained pathological scores." Using the DSSI/sAD with equally small numbers we have similarly found that of 31 long stay chronic schizophrenics only 31% did so. It is not, therefore, a suitable instrument for chronic schizophrenics.

Manic-Depressives in the manic phase would be expected to be notable, within the full DSSI, for their scores on the delusions of Grandeur and state of Elation sets. However, of 42 patients who endorsed the delusions of Grandeur set in Class 3, 71% reported themselves to be experiencing states of Depression and the same percentage states of Anxiety.

Some organics doubtless suffer states of Anxiety and/or of Depression, which should be picked up by the DSSI/sAD; but the Scale is not intended for use as a diagnostic instrument for this purpose. The same applies to psychosomatic disorders. The Scale can be used to ascertain the degree of anxiety and depression once the ulcer, the hypertension, the asthma or whatever has been identified.

Procedure

INSTRUMENT

The DSSI/sAD Scale consists of the following 14 items (of which numbers 1, 3, 4, 7, 9, 11 and 13 are the anxiety items):

1. Recently I have worried about every little thing.
2. Recently I have been so miserable that I have had difficulty with my sleep.
3. Recently I have been breathless *or* had a pounding of my heart.
4. Recently I have been so "worked up" that I couldn't sit still.
5. Recently I have been depressed without knowing why.
6. Recently I have gone to bed not caring if I never woke up.
7. Recently, for no good reason, I have had feelings of panic.
8. Recently I have been so low in spirits that I have sat for ages doing absolutely nothing.
9. Recently I have had a pain *or* tense feeling in my neck or head.
10. Recently the future has seemed hopeless.
11. Recently worrying has kept me awake at night.
12. Recently I have lost interest in just about *everything*.
13. Recently I have been so anxious that I couldn't make up my mind about the simplest thing.

14. Recently I have been so depressed that I have thought of doing away with myself.

Each item is scored 0, 1, 2 or 3 according to the degree of distress claimed, e.g. a little, a lot or almost unbearably. The possible range of scores is, therefore, from 0 to 42.

SUBJECTS

For this part of the programme the subjects were as follows:

(a) Normals: 136 adult subjects, 36 male and 100 female, have been examined. They comprised non-graduate hospital personnel, and members of various educational and recreational classes. The data on adolescents, referred to above, have been excluded.

(b) Psychiatric patients: These are the same 480 patients referred to earlier, for example, in Chapter 5. There were 118 out-patients, 109 day-patients and 253 in-patients—as far as possible, excluding chronic schizophrenics.

Validation

1. VALIDATION OF ITEM CONTENT

As discussed in Chapter 5, clinical psychologists and psychiatrists were asked to judge each of the full DSSI items. The rating task was in two parts. First, judges were given a pack of 84 filing cards (each bearing one item from the Inventory) and a rating form, on which were the following free-choice instructions: "Each card bears a psychiatric symptom, and on its reverse side a number. Please allocate each symptom to the *non-organic* syndrome that you feel is most appropriate. Write your choice of syndrome next to the symptom number on the rating form. If you cannot come to any decision put a question mark." The judges were told to use their own classificatory system. No nosological structure was imposed upon them.

After completing this, they were asked to read through the cards again and to "allocate each of the cards, by number, to one of the 12 syndromes below. Enter the item number against the syndrome that you think is appropriate or closest. Try to come to a choice for every item. Use the 'Other' category as little as possible." The results obtained for the 12 sets on this forced-choice method have been discussed in Chapter 5. The present concern is solely with the state of Anxiety and state of Depression sets.

Anxiety items

In the free-choice situation, 76% of the ratings of the Anxiety State items were in terms as "anxiety state" or "anxiety neurosis". Twelve percent of the choices were for variously named "depression" syndromes, 6% for undifferentiated "affective disorder" and 6% were divided among five other syndromes.

In the forced-choice situation, with the 12 DSSI syndromes plus the "Other" category from which to choose, Anxiety State was selected in 83% of cases. Twelve percent went to Neurotic Depression, leaving only 5% assigned elsewhere.

Depression items

The DSSI contains items related to two depression syndromes. The one which forms a part of the current sAD Scale, state of Depression, refers to depressed mood. The other group of items, delusions of Contrition, belongs to Class 3 (Integrated Delusions) within the hierarchy of classes of personal illness. The inclusive non-reflexive relationship between these two sets has been described in some detail elsewhere (Foulds, 1973; Foulds and Bedford, 1975a). In brief, all psychotic depressives (delusions of Contrition) are also neurotic depressives (states of Depression), whilst the converse does not hold. Theoretical distinctions apart, the frequency of endorsement of these items has been shown to be quite different. Wing *et al.*, (1974) make essentially the same distinction when presenting data on the clinical characteristics of the broad Catego classes of "depressive psychoses" and "neurotic depressions".

In the free-choice situation, 97% of the judgments included the word "depression". Seven different labels in all were used.

In the forced-choice situation, every choice fell into either the Neurotic Depression or the Psychotic Depression categories.

Total sAD *items.*

When the sAD Scale is viewed as a whole, rather than as two syndromes, it is pertinent to examine how the judges rate the 14 items. Of the free-choice judgments 96% were in terms of adverse mood change. Of the forced-choice judgments 98% fell into either the anxiety or into one of the two depressions categories.

It seems that the vast majority of ratings made by experienced clinical psychologists and psychiatrists are congruent with the contention that the sAD items refer to anxiety and depression as psychiatric mood disturbances.

2. VALIDATION OF ITEM SETS

It was possible to collect ratings by psychiatrists on 96 of their inpatients as to the degree of evidence for the presence of anxiety and depression. Four-point scales were used and scored thus: Outstanding (evidence)—3; "A lot"—2; "A little"—1; and "None"—0. In contrast to the previously mentioned raters, these were often junior staff members. The ratings and sAD testing were both undertaken during the first week of admission.

The results for Anxiety and Depression separately have already been given in Chapter 5. In both instances the relationship between ratings and sAD scores was significant. By combining the two sets of ratings it was possible to compare them with the patients' scores on the full 14 item scale. As only one person was given the maximum rating on both syndromes, this category was collapsed with those rated five.

Table 17 shows that the patients' scores, with the sole exception of those with a combined rating of 3, show a steady increase as rating scores increase. The F ratio is significant beyond the 1% level of confidence.

TABLE 17

Psychiatric Ratings and DSSI/sAD scores of 96 in-patients

Rated	n	Mean sAD	s.d.	
0	5	7·20	7·12	
1	19	11·84	9·71	
2	24	13·46	10·43	
3	20	13·10	7·62	For df $= 5,90$, F $= 3·2874$,
4	19	18·05	70·04	$p < 0·01$
5+	9	22·44	8·47	

It would seem that there is reasonable agreement between the self-ratings of patients of their anxiety and depression and the opinions of the psychiatrists treating them. Parenthetically it may be added that, given that some patients would be re-admissions (with a known case-note history) and many would be psychotics, it might have been expected that the doctors would tend to be less concerned with or aware of the "lesser" symptoms. In addition, some might have been diagnosed as lying within the personality universe of personality disorder. Contrary to expectation, the psychiatrists in fact ascribe absence (a rating of 0) in only 17% of cases for both anxiety and depression.

Homogeneity

The allotting of the anxiety and depression items by experienced raters affords a means of evaluating the homogeneity of these sets. Another approach is that of comparing the mean scores of the items and the percentages of positive endorsements. Table 18 provides these figures for all 14 items for normals and patients.

TABLE 18

Mean scores and percentage of positive endorsement of the sAD Scale items for normals and patients

Question	Normals (N = 136)			Patients (N = 480)		
	$\bar{X}$	s.d.	% 1+	$\bar{X}$	s.d.	% 1+
A 1	0·09	0·33	7·4	1·21	1·02	65·2
D 2	0·09	0·33	7·4	1·06	1·04	59·2
A 3	0·10	0·30	9·6	0·73	0·84	50·8
A 4	0·13	0·42	11·0	1·06	1·00	60·8
D 5	0·16	0·48	12·5	1·25	1·20	59·4
D 6	0·01	0·09	0·7	0·71	1·00	40·4
A 7	0·10	0·35	8·8	1·18	1·06	63·8
D 8	0·12	0·42	8·1	1·17	1·04	62·9
A 9	0·17	0·41	15·4	0·86	0·97	52·9
D10	0·12	0·37	10·3	1·36	1·14	68·7
A11	0·22	0·50	18·4	1·14	1·03	62·7
D12	0·10	0·40	6·6	1·18	1·08	62·1
A13	0·07	0·35	4·4	0·98	1·07	53·1
D14	0·04	0·19	3·7	0·82	1·01	47·5

The mean item score for normals is 0·11 (range 0·01 to 0·22); whilst that for patients is 1·05 (range 0·71 to 1·36). In comparing the percentages giving positive answers (1+) it is apparent that there is also some degree of spread. The normal subjects range from 0·7% to 18·4% and the patients from 40·4% to 68·7%. The higher normal sample and lower patient endorsements are somewhat mitigated by the fact that the least endorsed item (No. 6) is so for both samples, and that the most frequently endorsed item for normals (No. 11) is one of the highest among the patients. More generally, the Spearman rho between the ranks of the normals and patients mean score per item is 0·95. A comparison of the ranks by percentage scoring 1+ gives a rho of 0·88. Both correlations are significant (p < 0·0005, 1 tailed). It can also be added that there is a tendency, on the whole DSSI, for increasingly higher normal–patient differentiation to be found at each higher "degree of distress" claimed.

Additionally, one might consider the inter-correlations between the items of each set and the statistical relationship between the two syndromes. The first practice, as Maxwell (1972) has pointed out, often results in a difficult interpretative exercise within the universe of symptomatology because of the high percentage of zero scores. The distribution of scores will not be normal (and we have, indeed, shown that they are not) and product-moment correlations will be inflated. The patients' mean scores per item cited above are much higher than those given by Maxwell. As he was dealing with "psychotic" and "neurotic" items, this is not surprising. With this caution in mind, the range of Pearson Product-moment correlations within the anxiety items, for all 480 patients, is from 0·55 to 0·23 (mean r = 0·37±0·08). For the depression items the highest correlations is 0·65 and the lowest 0·32 (mean r = 0·46±0·09). All of these correlations are significant at least at the 1% level of confidence.

The product-moment correlations between the scores on the anxiety and depression sets are given at the foot of Table 19. They range from 0·61 to 0·73 and are all significant at least at the 0·1% level of confidence.

A final estimate of the common mutual occurrence of the two syndromes is the fact that, of the total 480 patients, 83% of those who exceeded the cutting point for anxiety did so for depression; and 86% of those who exceeded the cutting point for depression did so for anxiety. From here on, therefore, only the combined sAD Scale scores will be considered.

Distribution

The sAD scores of normal subjects are grossly abnormally distributed, as can be seen in Table 19. The kurtosis and skewness statistics are respectively 11·29 and 2·95 and the curve is J-shaped.

The sAD scores of patients are distributed in a totally different manner, though equally abnormally. If all 43 possible scores are considered, the resultant curve is a line almost parallel with the abscissa. In other words, most score points have an approximately equal endorsement rate. For comparison with normals the kurtosis and skewness figures for all patients are -0.80 and 0.25 respectively. Combining score points into class intervals gives a platykurtic distribution.

Stability-change

Unlike personality measures, which should remain relatively stable over time, illness or disturbance measures should change in the direction of remission with treatment. Sixty-eight patients were re-tested on the DSSI after one month (see Chapter 5). On the first occasion they had a mean score on sAD of 12.68 (s.d. 9.09) and, on the second occasion, of 6.40 (s.d. 8.33). The Sign Test (Siegel, 1956) gives a z of 5.1215 ($p < 0.00003$, one-tailed).

Although this result is not conclusive, in that no external estimate of psychiatric state was made, the evidence does suggest that the sAD is sensitive to change. In particular, it should be recognized that a few patients would seem to have become worse and rather more remained resistant to treatment. Both of these outcomes militate against detecting a significant change in the group as a whole.

Differentiation

Although any Personal Disturbance Scale must be highly discriminatory as between normal and patient groups, it would be unrealistic to expect all normals to score as non-personally ill. In any sample of normals some are likely to be out-patients, to be undergoing treatment by a General Practitioner, or simply to be "coping" in the absence of any formal treatment. The latter, in particular, may be reliant on their own resources and/or inter-personal supports. G. Jones in Wadsworth et al. (1971) noted that "An investigation of the incidence of psychological illness in a British general practice showed that about 10% of adult patients on a doctor's list will receive treatment in any one year for an unequivocal psychiatric complaint", and Brown et al. (1973) found "16% of the community sample suffering from a clear psychiatric disorder".

Whilst recognizing that epidemiological estimates of psychiatric illness in general populations vary widely, a possible criterion for selecting a cutting point on a personal disturbance measure might be that of ensuring that, say, about 15% of normals should be deemed psychiatrically ill, or at least disturbed.

Within a psychiatric hospital or clinic setting, as opposed to the more epidemiological survey usage, the conventional goal is to maximize the number of known patients positively identified. This might be expected to result in choosing a different, and lower, cutting point.

A third different decision might be made if the intersection point of the normal and patient score distributions was used. Besides maximizing the absolute number of "correct choices" this perhaps emphasizes the fact that we are using a two category system. "Organic" testing particularly has often included a borderline or undecided category. In coarse psychiatric screening this may be of real value and not just a means of allowing one to sit on the fence. It would seem reasonable to expect that there may be important psychological and sociological differences between those persons who do, and those who do not, seek treatment at this relatively lower level of distress. Mayo's (1969) work on the balance between intropunitive and extrapunitive attitudes, Brown's (1974) finding of the relevance of a supportive "significant other" and the general concept of "coping behaviour" are some of the more obvious possible factors in deciding who breaks down under stress.

Finally, there are, of course, many people who do not wish to use cutting points and prefer a dimensional approach to the assessment of illness-distress.

In order to accommodate the above points of view it was decided to present the DSSI/sAD data in such a way as to permit maximum flexibility. As always, cutting scores, when used, are best adapted to the requirements of any particular study.

Table 19 gives the percentages and cumulative percentages of sAD scores for the normal and patients groups, together with other descriptive statistics.

It can be seen that the scores of normal subjects are very predominantly at the zero end of the range, whilst the patients are roughly equally represented at all the score points within the restricted range shown here. The normal mean of 1·46 and median of 0 contrast markedly with the total patient mean of 14·60 and median of 14·68. Indeed, whilst only 3·7% of normals fall outside this Table (i.e. score 9+), approximately two-thirds of patients do so.

TABLE 19

Percentages and cumulative percentages of sAD scores for normal and patients groups

Scores	Normals n = 136 %	Normals % cum	In-patients n = 253 %	In-patients % cum	Out-patients n = 118 %	Out-patients % cum	Day-patients n = 109 %	Day-patients % cum	All-patients n = 480 %	All-patients % cum
0	50·0	50·0	4·7	4·7	2·5	2·5	1·8	1·8	3·5	3·5
1	22·8	72·8	4·3	9·0	4·2	6·7	0·9	2·7	3·5	7·0
2	9·6	82·4	3·2	12·2	7·6	14·3	5·5	8·2	4·8	11·8
3	3·7	86·1	4·3	16·5	0·8	15·1	3·7	11·9	3·3	14·1
4	2·2	88·3	4·3	20·8	5·1	20·2	2·8	14·7	4·2	19·3
5	5·1	93·3	3·2	24·0	2·5	22·7	0·9	15·6	2·5	21·8
6	2·2	95·6	4·3	28·3	4·2	26·9	0·9	16·5	3·5	25·3
7	0·7	96·3	4·3	32·6	3·4	30·3	1·8	18·3	3·5	28·8
8	0	96·3	2·4	35·0	8·5	38·8	1·8	20·1	3·7	32·5
Mean	1·46		14·27		13·59		16·47		14·60	
s.d.	2·54		9·83		9·01		8·74		9·43	
Median	0		13·56		13·50		16·92		14·68	
sA/sD r^s	0·61		0·73		0·68		0·63		0·69	

In order to retain the concept of "coping" we have, for our own purposes, adopted the following tentative convention:

Let scores of 0, 1 and 2 be considered non-personally disturbed ($\overline{PD}$);

Let scores of 3, 4 and 5 be considered personally disturbed (PD);

Let scores of 6 and above be considered personally ill (PI).

Table 20 shows the result of so doing.

TABLE 20

Percentages of normals' and of patients' sAD Scale scores falling into the three Personal Illness categories

Class	sAD scores	Normals n = 136	All patients n = 480
$\overline{PD}$	2—	82·4	11·8
PD	3, 4, 5	10·9	10·0
PI	6+	6·7	78·2

The "coping", or PD but not necessarily PI, category is seen to be found in an equal percentage of normals and patients. One might say, therefore, that an individual with a score of 3, 4 or 5 is much more likely to be able to "cope" than one with a score of 6 or more. Scores of 6 or more are, indeed, twelve times as often found among patients. Scores of 2 and below are more characteristic of normals by a frequency of about seven times.

Summary

A case has been made for the relevance of a short self-report inventory of distress, which, being derived from the Delusions-Symptoms-States Inventory, has a logical and empirical backing. Particular emphasis is laid upon the exclusive use of present state symptomatology, uncontaminated by personality attributes or aetiological speculations. The limitations of the sAD Scale are mentioned.

Data are presented which show statistically significant relationships between (a) patients' self-report on the inventory and their psychiatrists' ratings of their dysthymic states; and (b) the *a priori* allocation of the items to the syndromes and that of experienced raters.

Both at the item and total score levels a very high discrimination is found between the normal and patients groups. Comment is made on the changes in sAD scores over time and their abnormal distributions, both of which are in contrast to personality measures.

The scale would appear to be appropriate for the evaluation of treatments and for screening out the personally disturbed in general populations.

8

Personality and the Hierarchy

Personality and the hierarchy of illness classes

INTRODUCTION

In Chapter 5 data were presented which indicated that 93% of 480 psychiatric patients (excluding organics and illiterates) fitted the hierarchy of classes of personal illness on the Delusions-Symptoms-States Inventory. When psychiatrists rated for the presence of symptoms corresponding to the DSSI sets in 105 cases, 90% of these fitted the hierarchy. The relationship between the classes was an inclusive one in that almost all who belonged to Class 4 belonged also to Classes 3, 2 and 1; all who belonged to Class 3 belonged also to Classes 2 and 1; and almost all who belonged to Class 2 belonged also to Class 1. In addition, the relationship was non-reflexive in that not all who belonged to Class 1 belonged to Classes 2, 3 and 4; not all who belonged to Class 2 belonged to Classes 3 and 4; and not all who belonged to Class 3 belonged to Class 4.

The aim in the first part of this chapter is to determine whether certain more enduring personality attributes are related to the classes of personal illness.

If concern were solely with failure to *maintain* personal relationships, this would suggest that the illness itself rendered such maintenance more difficult; if concern were with the inability to *establish* personal relationships, this would suggest that long-standing personality difficulties had always hindered the development of personal relationships. Both factors might, of course, be operative, particularly in such disruptive illnesses as the functional psychoses. An individual suffering from a psychotic depression might have been more than normally self-critical before his illness, but have become even more so during the illness. The paranoiac may have been more than normally critical of others before the onset of his psychosis, but have become exceptionally so after the onset. If, however, one found that the personality variables remained relatively stable even when the symptoms had been considerably ameliorated, this would tend to favour the view that long-standing personality difficulties had hindered the development of adequate personal relationships.

PROCEDURE

When the symptom and personality measures are being compared, the number of normal subjects is 186—75 men and 111 women, with an average age of 27·56 years (s.d. 9·69)—and the number of patients drops to 325, without changing the nature of the sample in any significant way.

The 325 patients were allocated by the DSSI as follows: Class 4 = 34 (or 10·5%); Class 3 = 79 (24·3%); Class 2 = 115 (35·3%); Class 1 = 58 (17·9%); Class 0 = 39 (12·0%).

The Personality Deviance Scales (PDS) consist of three scales intended to measure Extrapunitiveness, Intropunitiveness and Dominance.

Although the actual items differ, the PDS is in part a modification of the Hostility-Direction of Hostility Questionnaire (Caine *et al.*, 1967) with some additions and omissions. Dominance has been added and Delusional Guilt and Projected Hostility dropped, as these latter belong more properly to the symptom-sign universe rather than the personality universe. Whereas the HDHQ was in a simple Yes/No format, the new scales are 4-point—Never, seldom, often, nearly always.

The Extrapunitive Scale consists of six items intended to assess hostile thoughts and six to assess denigration of other people. The Intropunitive Scale is made up of six items intended to measure lack of self-confidence and six to assess over-dependency, both of which at least strongly imply a self-critical attitude. The Dominance Scale comprises six items intended to assess dominance and six to assess overt or uninhibited aggression.

Correlations with 16PF Scales, Form A (Cattell *et al.*, 1970) afford some support for these formulations in a sample of 52 normal subjects with a mean age of 21·42 years±4·79. Studies are in progress for comparing the PDS with PEN (Eysenck and Eysenck, 1972) and EPI (Eysenck and Eysenck, 1964).

From Table 21 it can be seen that Extrapunitiveness is most highly correlated with suspiciousness (L) and self-sufficiency (Q_2); Intropunitiveness with low egostrength (C—), guilt proneness (O) and tenseness (Q_4); Dominance with dominance (E), surgency (F), forthrightness (N—) and venturesomeness (H).

TABLE 21

Pearson Product-Moment correlations between the Personality Deviance
Scales (PDS) and the 16PF for 52 normals

Extrapunitiveness and L	0·53	Q_2	0·41					
Intropunitivenes and C	—0·55	O	0·49	Q_4	0·48			
Dominance and E	0·54	F	0·47	N	—0·47	H	0·46
	p < 0·003 for the lowest correlation							

The correlations between the three PDS Scales among normals and patients are shown in Table 22.

TABLE 22

Correlations between Extrapunitiveness, Intropunitiveness and Dominance
for 186 normals and patients

	Normals		Patients	
Ex : In	0·12	n.s.	0·36	p < 0·001
Ex : Dom	0·20	p < 0·01	0·21	p < 0·001
In : Dom	—0·41	p < 0·001	—0·37	p < 0·001

All the correlations, except that between Extrapunitiveness and Intropunitiveness in the normal sample are significant at least at the 1% level of confidence. This finding of a much higher correlation among patients than among normals is in line with earlier findings with the Hostility-Direction of Hostility Questionnaire (Caine *et. al.*, *op. cit.*). The most likely explanation is that, whereas the normal individual can tolerate some expression of extrapunitiveness without undue guilt, the personally ill are intropunitive about their extrapunitiveness.

The correlations between Extrapunitiveness and Dominance, though significant, are relatively low; whereas those between Intropunitiveness and Dominance are relatively high in these samples, despite the fact that all three measures relate quite differently to the 16PF Scales. For that reason and because data are in hand which show that Dominance differentiates between certain groups where Intropunitiveness does not, it was decided at least for the time being to retain a three scale structure.

Split half-reliabilities were calculated for the 186 normals and the Spearman-Brown Prophecy Formula gave the following correlations: Extrapunitive, 0·80; Intropunitive, 0·84 and Dominance, 0·76. These were all significant well beyond the 0·1% level of confidence.

Table 23 shows the means and standard deviations for a group of 66 patients who were tested shortly after admission and again after one month. Re-test correlations are also given.

TABLE 23

Test and re-test means and correlations for 66 patients on the Personality Deviance Scales

	Extrapunitive Mean s.d.	Intropunitive Mean s.d.	Dominance Mean s.d.
Test	26·1 5·6	25·8 5·0	29·6 5·0
Re-test	27·1 2·4	26·5 5·8	29·1 5·0
Correlations	0·84	0·67	0·76
	All r^s significant at $p < 0.001$		

There were no significant differences between occasions on any measure. This, together with the reasonably high correlations, indicates that the three measures are rather stable over a period of one month, even in a sample of patients in which the symptom picture had changed very considerably. Seventy-two percent had changed their DSSI class, the great majority downwards. The stability of the personality measures held for both delusional and non-delusional patients; but this aspect requires investigation at the level of illness groups rather than merely at the level of illness classes. A further requirement is for re-testing at longer intervals than one month. It has, however, been shown that symptom measures change very considerably within one month; but the personality measures used here do not.

The two criteria which we have emphasized most for differentiating between personality and symptom measures have been stability—change and skewed—normal distributions. In Chapter 5, we showed that symptom measures changed very considerably in a month. In Chapter 7, we showed that all symptom measures were very markedly skewed among both patients and normals, with the possible exception of state of Anxiety and state of Depression for patients. These two distributions departed from normality, being decidedly platykurtic. In this chapter, we have shown that the three personality measures remained unchanged after one month. It now remains to show the score distributions for these three measures.

TABLE 24

Score distributions on Extrapunitiveness, Intropunitiveness and Dominance for 186 normals and 481 patients (percentages)

Score	Extrapunitive		Intropunitive		Dominant	
	N	P	N	P	N	P
12			1			
13						
14		1				
15		1		1		
16	1	2	2	1		1
17	1	2	2	1		1
18	2	2	1	2	1	1
19	2	3	4	4		3
20	3	5	6	3		2
21	1	4	4	2	2	4
22	3	4	8	6	6	6
23	4	6	7	5	3	4
24	11	5	11	6	4	6
25	10	6	9	5	5	5
26	13	8	12	6	6	7
27	7	6	8	7	7	9
28	10	6	4	3	10	8
29	5	7	3	6	11	6
30	4	4	7	9	6	5
31	5	6	4	5	9	7
32	7	5	1	4	6	4
33	2	4	1	4	6	3
34	1	1		2	4	4
35	2	2		3	2	3
36	1	3		3	2	3
37		2		2	4	2
38			1	2	2	1
39			2	2	1	1
40	1			1	1	1
41				1		
42				1		
43				1	1	
44 to 48						
Kurtosis	0·89	−0·08	1·05	−0·31	−0·08	−0·18
Skewness	0·02	0·15	0·39	0·24	0·25	0·15
Mean	26·52	26·50	25·01	28·21	29·31	27·70
s.d.	4·63	5·95	4·81	6·33	4·81	5·48
Median	26·26	26·38	24·87	27·89	29·05	27·45

It can be seen: (1) that the kurtosis and skewness values are rather low for both groups on all measures; but that the patient group tends to be somewhat more platykurtic; (2) that the means do not differ greatly between groups, except perhaps on Intropunitiveness; (3) that the medians are always quite close to the means throughout; and (4) that the standard deviations of patients are always appreciably higher. It may be concluded that the criterion of normal distribution in the normal population is well met. The vast differences between these six distributions and those derived from the DSSI are immediately apparent.

We now turn to the original question as to whether these particular personality measures are related in any meaningful way to the hierarchy of classes of personal illness.

Results. Table 25 shows the means and standard deviations of the 4 classes of personal illness, the not-personally ill patient group and normals.

TABLE 25

Means of normals and patients on Extrapunitiveness, Intropunitiveness and Dominance

Class	n	Extrapunitive $\bar{X}$	s.d.	Intropunitive $\bar{X}$	s.d.	Dominance $\bar{X}$	s.d.
4	34	30·56	5·62	30·47	5·07	25·41	5·08
3	79	27·58	6·33	28·73	7·55	28·04	6·20
2	115	26·77	5·28	27·83	5·91	27·93	5·11
1	58	23·88	5·39	26·66	6·01	26·78	5·20
0	39	22·21	4·07	26·03	4·85	26·95	4·55
Normal	186	26·52	4·62	25·01	4·81	29·31	4·81
F =		14·48		4·66		1·95	
p =		< 0·001		< 0·01		n.s.	

It can be seen that for Extrapunitiveness and Intropunitiveness the means of the classes are ranked 4, 3, 2, 1, 0, in line with the hierarchy. This does not apply to Dominance, where the F value is not significant. Whereas all classes are on the Intropunitive and Submissive sides of normal, they are divided on Extrapunitiveness. On this last measure, the means for the two psychotic classes are above normal, those for Dysthymic States and the not-personally ill below normal and that of Neurotics about the same as the normals. In all but one instance (Class 0 on Intropunitive) the variances for patients are higher than those of normals. Statistically deviant personalities should, therefore, be found more often in the patient sample, which was, of course, predicted.

Table 26 shows the percentage of normals and of the classes of patients who score 2 or more standard deviations above or below the normal mean on each of the measures.

TABLE 26

Percentage of normals and of the classes of patients deviating by ± 2 s.d.[s] from the normal mean on the PDS Scales

Class	n	Extrapunitive %+ %−		Intropunitive %+ %−		Dominance %+ %−	
4	34	18	0	21	0	3	15
3	79	13	6	22	0	7	16
2	115	5	3	17	3	3	4
1	58	3	16	12	3	2	10
0	39	0	21	3	3	0	5
Normal	186	2	4	3	2	3	1
Patients	325	7	8	16	2	2	8

It is clear from this Table that the differences between patients as a whole and normals is much less than between classes of patients and normals. It can be seen that high Intropunitiveness is the most discriminating and that low Intropunitiveness and high Dominance do not discriminate between normals and patients. In the light of these findings, an overall maladjustive personality deviance score, which might prove to have predictive value, was obtained as follows:

	Extrapunitive	Intropunitive	Dominance
Score 3 for a score of		35+	
Score 2 for a score of	36+ or 17−	33 or 34	19−
Score 1 for a score of	34/35 or 18/19		20/21/22

Table 27 shows the score distributions for normals and for the classes of patients.

For the percentage scoring 2+, the classes are again ranked in accordance with the illness hierarchy. All the differences between normals and the five classes of patients are statistically significant well beyond the 0·1% level of confidence, except for that between normals and the not-personally ill patients, which is at the 0·2% level. The respective Chi Squares (for 1 df) are as follows: Normals v. Class 4(DD) = 49·33;

TABLE 27

Maladjustive Personality Deviance scores of normals and the classes of
patients (percentages)

Score	Normals	Class 4	Class 3	Class 2	Class 1	Class 0	All patients
7	0	0	1·3	0	1·7	0	0·6
6	0	0	1·3	0·9	0	0	0·6
5	1·6	11·8	7·6	4·3	1·7	2·6	5·2
4	1·6	5·9	11·4	5·2	8·6	0	6·7
3	2·2	8·8	7·6	9·6	8·6	7·7	8·6
2	5·4	23·5	15·2	13·9	12·1	20·5	15·7
1	9·7	11·8	5·1	7·8	8·6	10·3	8·0
0	79·6	38·2	50·6	58·3	58·6	59·0	54·5
% 2+	10·8	50·0	44·4	33·9	32·7	30·8	37·5

Normals v. Class 3(ID) = 47·77; Normals v. Class 2(NS) = 24·14; Normals v. Class 1(DS) = 15·95; Normals v. Class 0($\overline{PI}$) = 10·59.

Thus, at the top of the illness hierarchy (Class 4), maladjustive Personality Deviance, as defined here, is almost five times as frequent as in the normal sample; at the bottom of the hierarchy (Class 0), it is still nearly three times as frequent.

DISCUSSION

It has been shown that both Extrapunitiveness and Intropunitiveness are related to the classes of personal illness in a way consistent with the illness hierarchy. If one assumes that these personality scales measure pre-morbid personality, do scores help to predict how far up the hierarchy a person is likely to go if he once becomes ill? The hierarchy hypothesis does not necessarily include any claim that people do move up the hierarchy, although this may well be so. We do not yet know; but we do know that they move down the hierarchy, whilst continuing to conform to it (see Chapter 5). We also now know that they retain very similar Extrapunitive, Intropunitive and Dominance scores after an interval of one month, despite a marked decrease in symptomatology. Should this stability be maintained over much longer periods, it would seem likely that these measures are, indeed, of pre-morbid personality. This is not, of course, to say that even then personality measures are absolutely immutable under all circumstances. It would, however, suggest that the task of bringing about desirable changes would be a great deal more difficult than the mere amelioration of symptoms. It would also be likely to be much more rewarding in terms of prevention of relapses.

If the personality scores were a consequence of particular forms of illness, one would expect them to co-vary with changes in illness status. They do not appear to do so. It could, however, be that the personality attitudes are exaggerated by the illness *and* take much longer to change. The issue must remain in doubt until longer follow-up periods have been investigated. Should it transpire that personality attitudes are ill-ness-affected, they would still provide more fundamental measures of clinical improvement than do symptom measures alone. Whatever may be the success rate of depth psychotherapists, they have at least aimed at the right target.

A great many more than 325 patients will be required to look for differences on the personality measures between all of the groups within classes and between groups between classes. In the meantime justifi-cations will be put forward for dichotomizing each of the illness classes on the basis of a single criterion. This reduces the number of groups from twelve to eight. Even so numbers in some of the rarer groups are inadequate. The results can, therefore, only be regarded as tentative. They do, however, appear to make good clinical sense and are perhaps on that account unlikely radically to be overturned.

Personality and illness groups

INTRODUCTION

Psychoanalysts have maintained that the various forms of psychiatric illness result from different modes of defence against anxiety. Failure to hold the defence at a certain point results in the development of a more serious form of illness. This view has much in common with the hierarchy of classes of personal illness which we have proposed.

Hilgard (1954), sympathetic to much of the psychoanalytic doctrine, has argued that defence can better be regarded as against guilt rather than anxiety and Hill (*op. cit.*) has written of the catastrophic lowering of self-esteem in depression. Helen Lynd (1958) sought to make a dis-tinction between guilt and shame. Guilt is experienced when someone does something against the moral, social or legal code which he knows will be disapproved of by others and probably by himself. Shame, on the other hand, is a more profound disturbance in which the individual questions his total worth as a person. Although many authors use the terms shame and guilt the opposite way round to Lynd, the mode of distinction is usually very similar. Shame, in Lynd's sense, may arise when attitudes emerge into consciousness which are utterly alien to the person's self-concept. When these attitudes are assimilated into an expanded self-concept, the opportunity exists for creative development of the person. The personally ill lack the self-assurance to face this opportunity. The potentiality for development is, therefore, denied them. So long as the ruminative obsessional persists in regarding his blasphemous thoughts as alien to his "real" self, he denies himself the opportunity of deepening his understanding of his relationship with his earthly father. To this extent his personal relationships are impoverished. Even the psychotic depressive, who protests his complete worthlessness and sinfulness, remains locked in an egocentric intropunitiveness. Our results perhaps suggest that people who develop a psychotic depression have always been low in self-esteem and that the "catastrophic lowering of self-esteem", to which Hill (*op. cit.*) refers, becomes manifest when delusions of sinfulness eventuate. When explanations are proferred by the patient for these feelings, they are usually patently vague or trivial. The "real cause" may be obscure to the clinician and almost certainly to the patient; but that there is one—or more—admits of little doubt. To this extent the psychotic depressive too has turned away from the possibility of creative development as a person.

We wish to argue that states of anxiety and/or of depression are the most common accompaniments and evasions of this deep underlying shame or potentially catastrophic lowering of self-esteem. From this position we wish to speculate that each of the classes of personal illness which we have proposed—delusions of disintegration, integrated delusions, neurotic symptoms and dysthymic states—might usefully be dichotomized, on the one hand, into those who retain in marked degree these anxiety or depressive states, no matter how they may displace the affect on to some "false cause" and, on the other hand, those who by repression and denial to a considerable extent rid themselves of these painful states.

We have noted earlier in this chapter that Intropunitiveness was most highly correlated with C, O and Q_4 in the 16PF—the three factors with the highest weightings on second-order Anxiety. We would, therefore, expect that those who retain most anxiety-depression will score higher on Intropunitiveness.

To be more specific, within the Integrated Delusions class, those with delusions of Contrition should retain anxiety-depression and score high on Intropunitiveness; those with delusions of Persecution or of Grandeur should not do so. We have already referred to delusions of Persecution and of Grandeur as exemplifying respectively extrapunitive and impunitive reactions. The paranoid patient is considered to be projecting blame, which might otherwise be self-directed, on to others. Even without such an interpretation, most clinicians would accept that paranoid patients are not given to blaming themselves. They may experience some anxiety about the threats to which they believe themselves to be subject; but this is very different in degree from that which psychotic depressives appear to experience. Manic patients are believed to be in flight from their problems and to over-compensate by developing an excessive self-esteem.

Within the delusions of Disintegration class, to the extent that the delusions are signs of non- or dis-integration, shame becomes virtually impossible, because identity and the sense of responsibility for one's own actions have largely been lost. Fortunately such an extremity is seldom reached and would, in any case, be beyond self-report methods of investigation. In other words, most of those with delusions of Disintegration also have Integrated delusions and it is perhaps here that the dichotomy within this class must be made. On the one hand, we have those with delusions of Contrition and, on the other hand, those with delusions of Persecution or of Grandeur and that very small minority with no Integrated delusions. These two groups should behave similarly to the corresponding groups within Class 3.

Within the Neurosis class, obsessionalism was long known as the guilt neurosis (Dalbiez, 1941) and phobias have only relatively recently been distinguished from obsessional neurosis. Phobics clearly retain anxiety, however displaced, and ruminatives retain anxiety and depression. Preventing compulsives from indulging in their rituals certainly exacerbates their anxiety; but Walker (1973) has argued very cogently that performance of the rituals by no means eliminates anxiety. We would expect, therefore, that these three groups would score high on anxiety-depression and on Intropunitiveness. Hysterics, on the other hand, have been taken as the paradigm for the impunitive reaction (Rosenzweig, *op. cit.*) and they have been shown to score relatively low on Intropunitiveness (Foulds, 1966). With their at least partial repression of painful affect and responsibility for their own actions, they would be expected to score relatively low on anxiety-depression and Intropunitiveness.

Within the Dysthymic States class, we have the states of Anxiety and of Depression in something nearer to pure culture as contrasted with states of Elation, the impunitives. Since states of Anxiety and of Depression are identified as such by their high scores on the DSSI, prediction is not possible; but they will clearly be expected to score higher on Intropunitiveness than will the state of Elation group.

If these speculations have substance, we can predict that, within each class, the "affective illnesses" should score significantly higher than the "non-affective" illness on the combined sets of the DSSI for state of Anxiety and state of Depression and on Intropunitiveness.

PROCEDURE

The subjects for this study were the same 325 patients as in the preceding study less the 39 who fell into Class 0, since these could not be dichotomized. The remaining 286 patients had all done both the DSSI and the PDS.

Within Class 4, the majority of cases scored on more than one of the Class 3 groups. It was, therefore, decided to make up the delusions of Contrition group with those who scored dC only and those whose dC score was higher than either dP or dG. This was designated group A ("Affective illness"). The Ā ("Non-affective illness") group was composed of those who did not fall into dC. A mixed group (M) contained those who were a mixture of dC and dP or dG, where one of the latter was higher than dC.

Within Class 3, group A consisted of those who scored 4 or more on dC only; group Ā consisted of those who scored 4 or more on dP and/or dG; group M was composed of those who scored 4 or more on dC and either dP or dG or both.

Within Class 2, group A was composed of those who scored 4 or more on any of Ps, CPs or Rs or any admixture of these; group Ā consisted of those who scored on CVs and/or Ds, but not on any of Ps, CPs or Rs; group M consisted of those who were a mixture of any group within Ps, CPs, Rs with any group within CVs and Ds.

Within Class 1, group A consisted of those who scored 4 or more on sA and/or sD; group Ā were those who scored 4 or more on sE alone; group M consisted of sA and/or sD with sE.

Thus, in each Class group A is expected to score significantly higher on sAD and Intropunitiveness than group Ā. No predictions were made with regard to Extrapunitiveness and Dominance.

RESULTS

Table 28 shows the means and standard deviations on the three PDS Scales and on DSSI sA+sD for the "affective", "non-affective" and "mixed" groups within each illness class.

In many instances the size of groups leaves much to be desired and work along these lines will clearly need to be continued. The results are certainly sufficiently encouraging to warrant this, since it can be seen that in every case group A scores significantly higher on Intropunitiveness and on sAD than does group Ā. When the total number of patients has been greatly increased, it will be possible to ascertain whether or not there are any differences within groups A and Ā.

TABLE 28

PDS and DSSI sAD scores of "affective" and "non-affective" and "mixed" groups within each illness class

		Extrapunitive $\bar{X}$ s.d.		Intropunitive $\bar{X}$ s.d.		Dominant $\bar{X}$ s.d.		DSSI/sAD $\bar{X}$ s.d.	
Class 4									
A	11	32.36	4.23	33.00	4.22	23.73	4.52	25.45	9.44
M	15	31.73	6.20	30.53	4.14	27.00	4.87	18.20	8.84
Ā	8	25.88	4.19	26.88	6.33	24.75	6.18	13.63	9.18
Class 3									
A	43	27.63	6.34	30.84	7.63	27.07	6.86	23.12	7.07
M	16	28.50	7.80	26.94	8.14	31.06	5.93	21.69	9.52
Ā	20	26.75	5.30	25.65	5.76	27.70	4.27	11.15	8.81
Class 2									
A	68	26.28	4.93	28.69	5.51	27.63	4.61	15.21	7.02
M	34	27.92	5.56	27.26	5.72	27.88	5.87	19.97	7.04
Ā	13	26.31	6.45	24.77	7.75	29.62	5.75	10.31	7.31
Class 1									
A	51	23.98	5.56	27.22	6.06	26.39	5.22	12.88	5.76
M	3	27.33	4.73	23.33	1.15	33.67	2.52	14.33	7.37
Ā	4	20.75	3.20	21.75	6.08	26.50	3.87	0.50	0.58
Normals									
	186	26.52	4.63	25.01	4.81	29.31	4.81		
4 A v Ā	t	3.31	p 0.01	2.54	0.05	0.42	NS	2.73	0.02
3 A v Ā	t	0.54	p NS	2.70	0.01	0.38	NS	5.78	0.001
2 A v Ā	t	0.02	p NS	2.19	0.05	1.37	NS	2.29	0.05
1 A v Ā	t	1.14	p NS	1.74	NS	0.04	NS	4.26	0.001

Table 29 shows the within-class correlations between the four measures. For this purpose Class 0 has been included.

H.N.P.I.—6*

TABLE 29

Within-class correlations between the four measures—Extrapunitiveness, Intropunitiveness, Dominance and sAD

N =	Class 4 34		Class 3 79		Class 2 115		Class 1 58		Class 0 39		All classes 325	
	r	p	r	p	r	p	r	p	r	p	r	p
Ex and In	−0.07	NS	0.31	0.01	0.38	0.001	0.26	0.05	0.48	0.002	0.35	0.001
Ex and Dom	0.08	NS	0.38	0.001	0.27	0.004	0.38	0.04	0.07	NS	0.26	0.001
Ex and sAD	0.38	0.03	0.04	NS	0.13	NS	0.24	NS	0.33	0.05	0.31	0.001
In and Dom	−0.50	0.003	−0.44	0.001	−0.29	0.002	−0.28	0.04	−0.31	NS	−0.35	0.001
In and sAD	0.19	NS	0.37	0.001	−0.01	NS	0.13	NS	0.40	0.02	0.24	0.001
Dom and sAD	−0.38	0.03	−0.19	NS	−0.04	NS	0.13	NS	0.05	NS	−0.07	NS

Extrapunitiveness and Intropunitiveness are significantly and positively correlated in all classes except for Class 4. Extrapunitiveness and Dominance were significantly and positively correlated in Classes 3, 2 and 1 and Extrapunitiveness and sAD in Classes 4 and 0. Intropunitiveness and Dominance were significantly and negatively correlated (i.e. with Submissiveness) in all but Class 0. Intropunitiveness and sAD were significantly and positively correlated only in Classes 3 and 0 and only 0·24 over all 325 subjects. Dominance and sAD was significantly and negatively correlated only in Class 4. Only in Classes 2 and 1 was the pattern of correlations alike.

DISCUSSION

Although roughly nine out of ten psychiatric patients can be said to score abnormally high on the combined DSSI sA and sD sets (for details see Chapter 7), reasons were advanced for dichotomizing each of the classes of personal illness into those who clinically appear to retain relatively more affect and those who retain relatively less. This was confirmed by the fact that within each illness class the "affect" group did score considerably higher than the "non-affect" group on DSSI sAD. The same relationship held for PDS Intropunitiveness, despite the fact that within-class correlations between sAD and Intropunitiveness were rather small. In addition, we have seen that sAD scores changed very markedly after a one-month interval; whereas Intropunitiveness did not. The two measures are, therefore, different; but both differentiate between the "affect" and "non-affect" groups whatever the class of illness. High Intropunitiveness alone is not sufficient to produce high sAD. Some additional factor, or factors, must be necessary; but high Intropunitiveness probably increases vulnerability to these other factors.

Summary

A sample of 325 psychiatric patients were allocated to classes within the hierarchy of personal illness by means of the Delusions-Symptoms-States Inventory. They were also given the Personality Deviance Scales. The results showed that, on Extrapunitiveness and Intropunitiveness, the classes were arranged in the same hierarchical order as on the DSSI. Maladjustive Personality Deviance (as statistically defined) was three and a half times as frequent among patients as among normals.

Patients with Delusions of Disintegration who also had delusions of Contrition scored considerably higher on Intropunitiveness and state of Anxiety-Depression than did those with Delusions of Disintegration and delusions of Persecution or delusions of Grandeur. The same applied to patients without Delusions of Disintegration. Those with delusions of Contrition scored much higher on the two measures than did those with delusions of Persecution or delusions of Grandeur.

Patients with Phobic, Compulsive or Ruminative symptoms scored much higher on Intropunitiveness and state of Anxiety-Depression than did patients with Conversion or Dissociative symptoms.

The results indicate that Hysterics, Paranoiacs, Manics and one possible sub-group of Schizophrenics are less anxious or depressed and less self-blaming than other groups of patients. They do not contravert the view that the former groups characteristically make use of the defence dynamisms of repression, denial and projection rather than of displacement, isolation and undoing; nor do they provide any additional support. On this supposition one would have to predict that removal of their major symptoms would exacerbate anxiety and self-blame at least in the short term. Change in this direction would not be expected for the "affective" groups of patients.

Whereas, in a mixed sample of patients, symptom measures changed considerably after one month, personality measures did not. Longer follow-up periods are required before it can be decided whether particular extreme personality scores predispose an individual to particular types of illness or whether the extreme scores are, at least in part, determined by the type of illness. Our guess is that both factors may be operative and that the latter may assume greater importance as one moves up the hierarchy. If such were the case, the degree of distortion of personality scores due to the current illness might prove to be a useful indicator of the severity of that illness. It would follow that changes on personality measures among patients who had become more or less symptom-free should be greater in the classes higher in the hierarchy.

9

Discussion and Conclusions

At the time of writing there was a story going the rounds about the
conflict in Northern Ireland. An air hostess announces: "Ladies and
gentlemen we will shortly be landing in Belfast. Will you please fasten
your safety belts and remember to put your watches back three hundred
years." Those who have heeded similar advice have succeeded in
demonstrating that the medical model then current does not adequately
reflect contemporary knowledge about either physical or mental illness;
but the death of the medical model has been greatly exaggerated. It
survives because it encompasses causative factors both within and without the organism, because it recognizes that more than one form of
treatment may be necessary for the alleviation of a particular illness
episode and that sometimes one type of treatment may be efficacious
in curing more than one type of illness.

Within the category of mental illness some psychiatrists and more
clinical psychologists have been less open-minded. They have often
claimed that one mode of approach is both necessary and sufficient for
the successful treatment of the entire range of mental, or personal, illness. The contribution which these single-minded schools will be able
to make to psychiatric treatment will be greatly enhanced when
modesty creeps in and they limit their field of operation.

The view has been taken that the term "illness" should be retained
as a convenient way of describing changes within the individual which
so diminish his ability to function in accordance with his own organic
or personal norms that intervention has been sought to counteract those
adverse changes. Without some such concept it becomes exceedingly
difficult to distinguish the personally ill from the personality disorders,
where emphasis has always been on the long-standing nature of the

disability and on the deviation from the norms of the general population.

We have adopted Macmurray's (1961) position that the person is inclusive of the organism and that we arrive at the concept "organism" by excluding attention from those characteristics which pertain uniquely to the person. The person has the capacity to intend the adoption of means to achieve imagined goals. He is capable, at least in part, of determining his own future. A number of statements by Bandura (1969) indicate that he accepts a somewhat similar position.

> Behavioural deficits also greatly restrict freedom of choice and otherwise curtail opportunities for self-direction.
>
> Some degree of freedom is possible within a deterministic view if it is recognized that a person's behaviour is a contributing factor to subsequent causal events. . . . From a social learning point of view freedom is not incompatible with determinism. Rather a person is considered free insofar as he can partly influence future events by managing his own behaviour.
>
> Granted that the selection of a particular course of behaviour from available alternatives is itself the result of determining factors, a person can nevertheless exert some control over the variables that govern his own choices.

At the organismic level the future is fully determinate. Application of a pencil to the sole of the foot will, with certain pathological exceptions, result in the turning up of the big toe. We may choose to initiate the process of walking; but we do not choose to take each step. The process is normally continued habitually, that is below the level of consciousness. The future is determinate.

At least since the time of William James it has been recognized that psychology is concerned with habitual behaviour. The psychologist seeks to unearth those constants which will enable him to predict an already determinate future. He has to exclude attention from those characteristics which pertain uniquely to the person. He cannot predict a future which is, at least in part, indeterminate; although, because it is only in part indeterminate, he can make intelligent guesses. We believe that psychologists have often made the mistake of regarding that to which they have rightly limited their attention as all there is to human nature.

The clinical psychologist is in somewhat different case from other psychologists. Although, like them, he has to limit his attention to habitual behaviour, he should still be able, as Macmurray (*op. cit.*) has pointed out, to give a much more complete account of the behaviour of his subjects, since it is characteristic of the personally ill that they have very largely lost those attributes which pertain uniquely to the person. A further difference lies in the fact that the clinical psychologist seeks not only to understand and predict the individual's habitual behaviour, but also to restore his capacity to enter into mutual personal relationships and, at least in part, to choose his own course of conduct. If the clinical psychologist (and, of course, the psychiatrist) is successful in doing this, the patient passes outside the range of his expertise. We regard the denial of this as a popular, current fallacy. One can only enter into a mutual personal relationship with a client as a person and not as a therapist. Clients are far too numerous to make this a practicable proposition. The limitation is not only, however, in the available time and stamina of the therapist, but in the nature of personal illness. One of the outstanding characteristics of the personally ill is their extreme egocentricity. They are so preoccupied with their own problems that little room is left for awareness of other people's problems. In many psychotics this preoccupation is so extreme that it is almost impossible to break through it to initiate even the most rudimentary communication. It is in such cases that physical methods of treatment are most effective and can rarely be equalled by psychological methods. In consequence of this, those therapists who have a pressing need to try to enter into mutual personal relationships with their clients have usually turned away from psychotic patients and often even from neurotic patients. They perforce end up by seeking out clients who are minimally ill, if ill at all, with whom their own needs can more nearly be fulfilled. What is disturbing is their apparent unawareness of the limitations they have imposed upon themselves. One of the consequences of this unawareness is their opposition to diagnosis. Naturally, if one confines one's practice to a rather homogeneous group of, at most, mildly ill patients, diagnosis is relatively unimportant and it becomes a shade less ridiculous to think of aetiology as lying entirely outside the organism; for those who deal with the whole range of personal illness diagnosis and multiple aetiology are inescapable.

What we have written of the clinical psychologist applies equally to the psychiatrist in that he too is in a favourable position to give a rather complete account of the behaviour of his subjects. He has the additional complication of being medically trained. As a medical man his aim is to restore the normal functioning of the organism. Since the physically ill are known to be at greater risk with regard to psychological illness and since half the patients seen by General Practitioners are personally disturbed, medicine would appear signally to have failed to shoulder its responsibilities to society. Prestige in medicine is in inverse relation to distance from the person. Psychiatry is still regarded as the Cinderella of medicine. Who, one wonders, are the Ugly Sisters? If the organism is necessary, but subordinate to the person, we need radically to re-orientate our evaluation of the various specialties, to concentrate more attention on enabling as many people as possible to live fully as persons and to reduce the morbid preoccupation with merely keeping organisms alive. In fairness it must, however, be said that if we end up with trans-planted teeth, kidneys, hearts and whatever else the future has in store for us, this may help to delimit the problem of what constitutes a person.

We have used the term "personal illness" to emphasize that what has changed for the worse in psychiatric patients are those characteristics which pertain uniquely to the person. Whilst admiring Kendell's (1975) ingenious application of Scadding's (1967) concept of "biological dis-advantage" to psychiatric illness, we regard it as insufficiently radical. We have rejected the idea that mental illness is but a poor and mislead-ing analogy with physical illness and the idea that it is a myth. If we are to think in terms of analogies, it would be more accurate to say that physical illness is a poor and misleading analogy with mental illness.

We have proposed a hierarchy of classes of personal illness and our review of the literature has indicated that this proposal is not new, although it has seldom been made explicit. What does appear to have been lacking is a systematic application of the idea to the whole range of personal illness and it is this which we have tried to supply.

We have suggested that it may prove helpful to regard personal ill-ness as divisible into four classes, each with its constituent groups, and that these classes are linked by a series of inclusive, non-reflexive, re-lationships. The class lowest in the hierarchy we have called Dysthymic States, since members of this class suffer from states of Anxiety and/or of Depression and/or of Elation; but they do not suffer from the symp-toms and signs characteristic of the classes higher in the hierarchy. The second class has been named Neurotic Symptoms, an inadequate term which it is probably too late to replace. The members of this class suffer from Conversion, Dissociative, Phobic, Compulsive or Ruminative symptoms in addition to one or more of the Dysthymic States. The third class we have called Integrated Delusions. Members of this class suffer from delusions of Persecution (extrapunitive) and/or Grandeur (impunitive) and/or Contrition (intropunitive) in addition to one or more of the groups of Neurotic Symptoms and one or more of the groups of Dysthymic States. The class highest in the hierarchy we have termed Delusions of Disintegration. We have not as yet decided what groups, if any, there should be; but members of this class suffer from hallucinations and delusions of passivity and of influence in addition to one or more type of Integrated Delusion, one or more type of Neurotic Symptom and one or more type of Dsythymic State.

The self-report Delusions-Symptoms-States Inventory was constructed to parallel exactly the 12 groups mentioned above. Each set consists of seven items. Any item which was affirmed by a subject was scored 1, 2 or 3, according to the degree of distress occasioned or the frequency of occurence or the certainty of belief. A cutting score between 3 and 4 was decided upon in advance of the data. Those who scored 4 or more on any set were allocated to that set and to the class in which that set fell. The final allocation, or DSSI diagnosis, was to the class highest in the hierarchy and to the group within that class. Using this method with the four classes and a fifth "symptom-free" class, there are 16 possible class patterns. Five of these patterns conform to the hierarchy and 11 do not. Table 30 shows these 16 patterns and the percentage of the 480 patients who fell into each of the patterns. It can be seen that just over 93% fell into the patterns which conformed with the hierarchy and that there was one non-fitting pattern (0101) which was much more common than the others. Clearly many more cases will be required be-

TABLE 30

Percentage of 480 patients falling into each Class pattern

Conforming to hierarchy					Not conforming				
	DD	ID	NS	DS	%	DD	ID	NS	DS	%
Disintegrative Delusions	1	1	1	1	8·1	0	1	0	1	2·9
Integrated Delusions	0	1	1	1	19·0	0	0	1	0	1·0
Neurotic Symptoms	0	0	1	1	34·2	0	1	1	0	0·8
Dysthymic States	0	0	0	1	17·9	1	0	1	1	0·6
Not personally ill	0	0	0	0	14·2	1	0	0	1	0·4
						1	1	1	0	0·2
						1	0	1	0	0·2
						1	1	0	0	0·2
						0	1	0	0	0·2
						1	1	0	1	0·0
						1	0	0	0	0·0

fore one can investigate the significance of particular non-fitting patterns.

Of 45 subjects with Delusions of Disintegration only 13% did not have Integrated Delusions; 7% did not have Neurotic Symptoms; and 7% did not have a Dysthymic State.

Of 106 subjects who had Integrated Delusions (but not Delusions of Disintegration) 14% did not have Neurotic Symptoms and 5% did not have a Dysthymic State.

Of 168 subjects who had Neurotic Symptoms (but no delusions of either type) only 2% did not have a Dysthymic State.

Those with Delusions of Disintegration tended to have more than one type of Integrated Delusion; whereas those who had Integrated Delusions, but not Delusions of Disintegration, tended to have one type of Integrated Delusion only. This held throughout the hierarchy. Virtually all those with Integrated Delusions had Neurotic Symptoms and characteristically more than one type of neurotic symptom; whereas those who had Neurotic Symptoms, but not Integrated Delusions, tended to have one, or certainly not more than two types of neurotic symptom. Finally, those with Neurotic Symptoms almost invariably had more than one type of Dysthymic State; whereas those with a Dysthymic State, but not Neurotic Symptoms, were as likely as not to have one type of Dysthymic State only.

This overspill of symptoms in classes below the individual's highest class may conceivably be an indication that his defences at these lower levels have not been adequate for enabling him to hold any of these positions. He has, therefore, perforce had to develop more unrealistic defences. If such were the case, it may be that those with mixed syndromes in their highest class are more likely than those with unmixed syndromes subsequently to move up the hierarchy.

If one makes no use at all of a hierarchical principle, the amount of overlap between syndromes is so great as to render the very concept of syndromes valueless. Under these circumstances only 13% of patients are classifiable in one syndrome only. For the remaining 87% of cases there are no adequate public rules for deciding which syndrome should be chosen for the final diagnosis. Although in recent years research workers in Britain (such as Wing and his collaborators, 1974) and in the United States (such as Spitzer and his collaborators, 1973) have shown that reliable diagnosis can be made, routine clinical diagnostic practice still remains unsatisfactory. Even if, as we believe, clinicians vacillate between applying a hierarchical principle, invoking the comparative adjective "more severe" without any clear referent and opting for their favourite diagnosis (usually the one they consider they can most easily treat), it is not difficult to understand the rather unsatisfactory inter-judge reliability figures.

Systematic application of the proposed hierarchy would provide a public rule and would, we suggest, be likely to produce a considerable improvement in diagnostic reliability. The fact that members of a particular class tend to have more than one type of syndrome within classes lower in the hierarchy does not involve any confusing overlap of syndromes, since the syndrome within the highest class takes precedence.

Evidence has been presented which indicates that there is a reduction in the number of symptoms in the majority of patients in as short a time as one month. Such patients continue nevertheless to conform to the hierarchy. From this it is clear that symptoms lower in the hierarchy do not improve before those higher in the hierarchy. We have, in consequence, speculated that it may be desirable to change the type of treatment as the patient moves down the hierarchy to whatever is considered to be the most appropriate for the new condition.

A Personal Disturbance Scale, consisting of the state of Anxiety and the state of Depression sets of the Delusions-Symptoms-States Inventory, has been used as a screening instrument. Since we have shown that nearly all patients suffer from a state of Anxiety and/or Depression this is a logical derivation, which is both economical and about as efficient as using the whole DSSI for this purpose.

Criteria for differentiating between signs, symptoms and states on the one hand and normal and deviant traits and attributes on the other have been discussed. Before going on to mention some of the findings obtained from the Personality Deviance Scales, it may be helpful to provide a brief summary of some of the differentiae between and within the universe of Personal Symptomatology and Personality Deviance.

Within Personal Symptomatology

Personal Symptomatology v. Personal Health. The presence of psychotic or neurotic symptoms or dysthymic states.

Personal Illness v. Personal Disturbance. The inability to cope in the community without professional help.

Neurosis v. Dysthymic State. Neurosis is inclusive of Dysthymic States and neurotic symptoms are more alien to the habitual self-concept.

Integrated Psychosis v. Neurosis. Integrated Psychosis is inclusive of Neurosis, but with the addition of delusions implying a grossly distorted self-concept.

Non-integrated Psychosis v. Integrated Psychosis. Non-integrated Psychosis is inclusive of Integrated Psychosis, but with the addition of delusions implying a marked loss of self-concept.

Psychosis v. Neurosis. Psychosis is inclusive of Neurosis, but with the addition of delusions, including hallucinations.

Within the Personality universe

Personality Deviance v. Normal Personality. The presence of a score on one or more personality dimension which is, say, at least two standard deviations above or below the normal mean.

Maladjustive v. Adjustive Personality Deviance. The presence of deviant attitudes which lead to the disruption of personal relationships or social processes as opposed to attitudes which indicate an unusual degree of concern for others as persons. The emphasis is, therefore, on egocentricity v. allocentricity.

Personality Disorder v. Discordant Personality. Within Maladjustive Personality Deviance, the inability to cope in the community without professional help or restraint.

Between universe differentiae

Personality v Personal Symptomatology. The presence in the general population of a normal rather than a skewed score distribution and of a stable rather than a changing measure over time. Personality attitudes will tend to be relatively ego-syntonic; whereas symptoms will tend to be distressful.

The Personality Deviance Scales were designed to measure Extrapunitiveness, Intropunitiveness and Dominance. Some support for these formulations was provided by their correlations with certain of the factors from the 16PF. The results showed that on Extrapunitiveness and on Intropunitiveness those with Delusions of Disintegration scored higher than those with Integrated Delusions, who scored higher than those with Neurotic Symptoms, who scored higher than those with Dysthymic States, who scored higher than those who were symptom-free. The classes were, therefore, arranged in the same hierarchical order as on the DSSI.

Maladjustive Personality Deviance (as statistically defined) was three and a half times as frequent among patients as among normals.

Whereas, in a mixed sample of patients, symptom measures changed considerably after one month, personality measures did not. Longer follow-up periods are required before it can be determined whether particular extreme personality scores predispose an individual to particular types of illness or whether the extreme scores are, at least in part, determined by the type of illness. Our guess is that both factors may be operative and that the latter may assume greater importance as one moves up the hierarchy. If such were the case, the degree of distortion of personality scores due to the current illness might prove to be a useful indicator of the severity of that illness. It would follow that changes on personality measures among patients who had become more or less symptom-free should be greater in the classes higher in the hierarchy.

Some tentative results obtained from dichotomizing each of the DSSI classes may prove to be of value if replicated on larger numbers. Patients with delusions of Disintegration who also had delusions of Contrition scored considerably higher on Intropunitiveness and state of Anxiety-Depression than did those with delusions of Disintegration and delusions of Persecution or of Grandeur. The same applied to patients in Class 3 (i.e. without delusions of Disintegration). Those with delusions of Contrition scored much higher on the same two measures than did those with delusions of Persecution or of Grandeur.

Patients with Phobic, Compulsive or Ruminative symptoms scored much higher on Intropunitiveness and state of Anxiety-Depression than did those with Conversion or Dissociative symptoms.

Patients with states of Anxiety or Depression scored considerably higher on Intropunitiveness than did those with a state of Elation.

The results indicate, therefore, that Hysterics, Paranoiacs, Manics and one possible group of Schizophrenics are less anxious or depressed and less self-blaming than other groups within their respective classes. These results do not contravert the view that the former groups characteristically make use of the defence dynamisms of repression, denial and projection rather than of displacement, isolation, and undoing; nor do they provide any additional support. On this supposition one would have to predict that removal of their major symptoms would exacerbate anxiety and self-blame at least in the short term. Changes in this direction would not be expected for the "affective" groups of patients.

At first sight self-esteem may appear to be at the low end of the Intropunitive dimension. We are inclined, however, to the view that it lies in the middle range and that extremely low scores are an indication of Impunitiveness, that is an inability to tolerate any self-criticism. Only 1·6% of normals score 2 or more standard deviations below the normal mean; whereas the corresponding figure for the "non-affective" group of Schizophrenics, Paranoids, Manics, Hysterics and Hypomanics combined is 6·7%.

We have noted that Hill (1968) has claimed that it is the catastrophic lowering of self-esteem which triggers the depressive mechanism. We believe that it may be the *threat* of a catastrophic lowering of self-esteem which triggers all non-organic psychiatric illnesses and that the various forms of illness are in part the resultant of different modes of defence against this threat. We agree, therefore, with Hill that "knowledge of the processes by which self-esteem is normally maintained becomes a vital matter for us". It seems probable that self-esteem, like happiness, is not something to be sought consciously and directly, but is more appropriately a by-product of the successful exercise of social and perhaps occupational skills. Successful artists, craftsmen, parents, lovers and friends all have in common a deep concern with something other than oneself. May be the greatest safeguard against personal illness is the ability to "love thy neighbour as thyself", the ability to enter into and maintain mutually satisfying personal relationships. From this it would appear to follow that the two fundamental functions of psychiatrists and clinical psychologists should be to increase understanding of the attitudes, interests, values and personal relationships of those who are widely acknowledged to be leading more than usually satisfying lives and to help those who are abnormally unsuccessful to remove the obstacles to so doing. In this latter endeavour it may be most profitable to focus attention on what it is that threatens the individual's self-esteem.

References

Adams, H. (1964). "Mental illness" or interpersonal behaviour? *American Psychologist*, **19**, 191–197.

Aitken, C. B., Buglass, D. and Kreitman, N. (1969). The changing pattern of attempted suicide in Edinburgh 1962–67. *British Journal of Preventive and Social Medicine*, **23**, 111–115.

Ausubel, D. P. (1961). Personality disorder is disease. *American Psychologist*, **16**, 69–74.

Bandura, A. (1969). "Principles of Behaviour Modification." Holt, Rinehart & Winston, New York.

Bannister, D. (1960). Conceptual structure in thought-disordered schizophrenics. *Journal of Mental Science*, **106**, 1230–1249.

Bannister, D. (1962). The nature and measurement of schizophrenic thought disorder. *Journal of Mental Science*, **108**, 825–842.

Bannister, D. and Fransella, Fay. (1966). A grid test of schizophrenic thought disorder. *British Journal of Social and Clinical Psychology*, **5**, 95–102.

Bannister, D. and Salmon, Phyllida. (1966). Schizophrenic thought disorder: specific or diffuse? *British Journal of Medical Psychology*, **39**, 215—219.

Bannister, D. and Fransella, Fay. (1967). "A Grid Test of Schizophrenic Thought Disorder". Psychological Test Publications, Barnstaple.

Bannister, D. and Mair, J. M. M. (1968). "The Evaluation of Personal Constructs". Academic Press, London and New York.

Berrington, W. P., Liddell, D. W. and Foulds, G. A. (1956). A re-evaluation of the fugue. *Journal of Mental Science*, **102**, 280–286.

Blackburn, Ivy. (1972). "A Psychometric Study of Unipolar and Bipolar Affective Disorders". Unpublished PhD. thesis, University of Edinburgh.

Bleuler, E. (1950). "Dementia Praecox". Allen & Unwin, London.

Breakey, W. R. and Goodell, Helen. (1972). Thought Disorder in Mania and Schizophrenia evaluated by Bannister's Grid Test for Schizophrenic Thought Disorder. *British Journal of Psychiatry*, **120**, 391–395.

Bromberg, W. (1954). "Man Above Humanity". Lippincott, Philadelphia.

Brown, G. W. (1974). "Social Class and Psychiatric Disorder". Paper given at the Department of Psychiatry, University of Edinburgh.

Brown, G. W., Sklair, P., Harris, T. O. and Birley, J. L. T. (1973). Life-events and psychiatric disorders, Part 1: Some methodological issues. *Psychological Medicine*, **3**, 74–87.

Bruner, J. S. (1956). A cognitive theory of personality. *Contemporary Psychology*, **1**, 355–356.

Caine, T. M., Foulds, G. A., and Hope, K. (1967). "Manual of the Hostility-Direction of Hostility Questionnaire (HDHQ)". University of London Press, London.

Cameron, N., (1963). "Personality Development and Psychopathology". Houghton Mifflin, Boston.

Cattell, R. B., Eber, H. W. and Tatsuoka, M. M. (1970). "Handbook for the Sixteen Personality Factor Questionnaire (16PF)". IPAT, Champaign, Illinois.

Chapman, J. (1966). The early symptoms of schizophrenia. *British Journal of Psychiatry*, **112**, 225–251.

Chapman, J. and McGhie, A. (1964). Echopraxia in schizophrenia. *British Journal of Psychiatry*, **110**, 365–374.

Clark, J. A. and Mallett, B. L. (1963). Follow-up study of schizophrenia and depression in young adults. *British Journal of Psychiatry*, **109**, 491–499.

Comrey, A. L. (1970). "EITS Manual for the Comrey Personality Scales". Educational and Industrial Testing Service, San Diego.

Coppen, A. and Metcalfe, Maryse. (1965). Effect of a depressive illness on M.P.I. scores. *British Journal of Psychiatry*, **111**, 236–239.

Crown, S. and Crisp, A. H. "Manual of the Middlesex Hospital Questionnaire (MHQ)". Psychological Test Publications, Barnstaple.

Dalbiez, R. (1941). "Psychoanalytic Method and the Doctrine of Freud". Vol. 1. Longmans, London.

Dixon, P. M. (1968). "Reduced Emotional Responsiveness in Schizophrenia". Unpublished PhD. thesis, University of London.

Eysenck, H. J. (1947). "Dimensions of Personality". Routledge & Kegan Paul, London.

Eysenck, H. J. (1960). "Handbook of Abnormal Psychology". Pitman Medical, London.

Eysenck, H. J. and Eysenck, S. B. G. (1964). "Manual of the Eysenck Personality Inventory". University of London Press, London.

Eysenck, H. J. (1968). A dimensional system of psychodiagnostics, in Mahner, A. R. (Ed). "New Approaches to Psychodiagnostic Systems", Aldine: New York.

Eysenck, S. B. G. and Eysenck, H. J. (1969). Scores on three personality variables as a function of age, sex and social class. *British Journal of Social and Clinical Psychology*, **8**, 69–76.

Eysenck, S. B. G. and Eysenck, H. J. (1972). The questionnaire measurement of psychoticism. *Psychological Medicine*, **2**, 50–55.

Eysenck, H. J. and Rachman, S. (1965). "The Causes and Cures of Neurosis". Routledge & Kegan Paul, London.

Feuchtersleben, E. von. (1845). "The Principles of Medical Psychology, Being the Outlines of a Course of Lectures by Baron Ernst von Feuchtersleben (1845)". Revised and edited by B. G. Babington, 1847. Sydenham Society, London. *Quoted in* "Three Hundred Years of Psychiatry", by R. Hunter and Ida Macalpine. Oxford University Press, London.

Fish, F. J. (1962). "Schizophrenia". J. Wright & Sons, Bristol.

Foulds, G. A. (1951). Temperamental differences in Maze performance. I. Characteristic differences among psychoneurotics. *British Journal of Psychology*, **42**, 209–217.

Foulds, G. A. (1964). Personal continuity and psychopathological disruption. *British Journal of Psychology*, **55**, 269–276.

Foulds, G. A. (1965). "Personality and Personal Illness". Tavistock, London.

Foulds, G. A. (1966). Psychic-Somatic symptoms and hostility. *British Journal of Social and Clinical Psychology*, **5**, 185–189.

Foulds, G. A. (1968). Neurosis and character disorder in hospital and in prison. *British Journal of Criminology*, **8**, 46–49.

Foulds, G. A. (1971). Personality deviance and personal symptomatology. *Psychological Medicine*, **1**, 222–233.

Foulds, G. A. (1973). The relationship between the depressive illnesses. *British Journal of Psychiatry*, **122**, 531–533.

Foulds, G. A. and Bedford, A. (1975). Hierarchy of classes of personal illness. *Psychological Medicine*, **5**, 181–192.

Foulds, G. A. and Bedford, A. (1976). The classification of depressive illness: a re-evaluation. *Psychological Medicine*, **6**, February.

Foulds, G. A. and Hope, K. (1968). "Manual of the Symptom-Sign Inventory". University of London Press, London.

Foulds, G. A., Hope, K., McPherson, F. M. and Mayo, P. R. (1967). Cognitive disorder among the schizophrenias, I. *British Journal of Psychiatry*, **113**, 1361–1368.

Freud, S. (1936). "The Problem of Anxiety". Norton, New York.

Gittleson, N. L. (1966a). The effect of obsessions on depressive psychosis. *British Journal of Psychiatry*, **112**, 253–260.

Gittleson, N. L. (1966b). The fate of obsessions in depressive psychosis. *British Journal of Psychiatry*, **112**, 705–708.

Goldberg, D. (1972). "The Detection of Psychiatric Illness by Questionnaire." Oxford University Press, London.

Goldberg, D. (1973). "The Relationship Between Depression and Anxiety". Paper given at the Department of Psychiatry, University of Edinburgh.

Gruenberg, E. (1969). How can the new Diagnostic Manual help? *International Journal of Psychiatry*, **7**, 368–374.

Hall, C. S. and Lindzey, G. (1957). "Theories of Personality". Wiley, New York.

Harding, D. W. (1953). "Social Psychology and Individual Values". Hutchinsons, London.

Hare, E. H. and Shaw, G. K. (1965). "Mental Health on a New Housing Estate". Oxford University Press, London.

Henderson, D. K. (1947). "Psychopathic States". Norton, New York.

Henderson, D. K. and Gillespie, R. D. (1946). "Textbook of Psychiatry". Oxford University Press, London.

Hilgard, E. R. (1954). Human motives and the concept of self. *In* "The Study of Personality". (Ed. H. Brand). Wiley, New York. Chapman & Hall, London.

Hill, Sir Denis. (1968). Depression: disease, reaction, or posture? *American Journal of Psychiatry*, **125**, 445–457.

Hornstra, R. (1962). "The Psychiatric Hospital and the Community". Paper read at the Annual Workshop in Community Mental Health, Pisgah View Ranch, Candler, North Carolina, June 11–21.

Jackson, B. (1970). The revised diagnostic and statistical manual of the APA. *American Journal of Psychiatry*, **127**, 65–73.

Jaspers, K. (1963). "General Psychopathology". Manchester University Press, Manchester.

Kapur, R. L., Kapur, M. and Carstairs, G. M. (1975). Indian Psychiatric Survey Schedule (IPSS). *Social Psychiatry*, **9**, 71–76.

Karpman, B. (1941). On the need of separating psychopathy into two distinct clinical types: the symptomatic and the idiopathic. *Journal of Criminal Psychopathology*, **3**, 112–137.

Kellner, R. (1971). I. Improvement criteria in drug trials with neurotic patients. *Psychological Medicine*, **1**, 416–425.

Kellner, R. (1972). II. Improvement criteria in drug trials with neurotic patients. *Psychological Medicine*, **2**, 73–80.

Kelly, G. A. (1955). "The Psychology of Personal Constructs". Norton, New York.

Kelly, G. A. (1958). Man's construction of his alternatives. *In* "Assessment of Human Motives" (Ed. G. Lindzey). Holt, Rinehart & Winston, New York.

Kendell, R. E. (1975). The concept of disease and its implications for psychiatry. *British Journal of Psychiatry*, **127**, 305–315.

Kendell, R. E. and DiScipio, W. J. (1968). Eysenck Personality Inventory scores of patients with depressive illnesses. *British Journal of Psychiatry*, **114**, 767–770.

Kreitman, N., Sainsbury, P., Morrisey, J., Towers, J. and Scrivener, J. (1961). The reliability of psychiatric assessment: an analysis. *British Journal of Psychiatry*, **107**, 887–908.

Lynd, H. M. (1958). "On Shame and the Search for Identity". Routledge & Kegan Paul, London.

Macmurray, J. (1961). "Persons in Relation". Faber & Faber, London.

Makhlouff-Norris, F. and Jones, H. G. (1971). Conceptual distance indices as measures of alienation in obsessional neurosis. *Psychological Medicine*, **1**, 381–387.

Marks, I. M. (1965). "Patterns of Meaning in Psychiatric Patients". Oxford University Press, London.

Mayo, P. R. (1969). Women with neurotic symptoms who do not seek treatment. *British Journal of Medical Psychology*, **42**, 165–169.

Maxwell, A. E. (1972). Difficulties in a dimensional description of symptomatology. *British Journal of Psychiatry*, **121**, 19–26.

Maxwell, A. E. (1973). Psychiatric illnesses: some inferences from symptomatology. *British Journal of Psychiatry*, **122**, 251–258.

McPherson, F. M. (1969). Thought-process disorder, delusions of persecution and non-integration in schizophrenia. *British Journal of Medical Psychology*, **42**, 55–57.

McPherson, F. M., Barden, Valerie, Hay, A. J., Johnstone, D. W. and Kushner, A. W. (1970a). Flattening of affect and personal constructs. *British Journal of Psychiatry*. **116**, 39–43.

McPherson, F. M., Barden, Valerie and Buckley, Felicity. (1970b). The use of "psychological" constructs by affectively flattened schizophrenics. *British Journal of Medical Psychology*, **43**, 291–293.

McPherson, F. M. and Buckley, Felicity. (1970c). Thought-process disorder and personal construct sub-systems. *British Journal of Social and Clinical Psychology*, **9**, 380–381.

McPherson, F. M., Buckley, Felicity and Draffan, Joan. (1971a). "Psychological" constructs, thought-process disorder and flattening of affect. *British Journal of Social and Clinical Psychology*, **10**, 267–270.

McPherson, F. M., Buckley, Felicity and Draffan, Joan. (1971b). "Psychological" constructs and delusions of persecution and "non-integration" in schizophrenia. *British Journal of Medical Psychology*, **44**, 277–280.

McPherson, F. M., Blackburn, Ivy, Draffan, Joan and McFadyen, M. (1973). A further study of the Grid Test of Thought Disorder. *British Journal of Social and Clinical Psychology*, **12**, 420–427.

Mellsop, G. W., Spelman, M. S. and Harrison, A. W. (1971). The performance of manic patients on the Grid Test for Schizophrenic Thought Disorder. *British Journal of Psychiatry*, **118**, 671–673.

Meyer, V. and Chesser, E. S. (1970). "Behaviour Therapy in Clinical Psychiatry". Penguin, Harmondsworth.

Milton, O. and Wahler, R. G. (1969). Perspectives and trends. *In* "Behaviour Disorders" (Ed. Milton and Wahler.) Lippincott, New York and Philadelphia.

Mischel, W. (1968). "Personality Assessment". Wiley, New York.

Mowrer, O. H. (1960). "Learning Theory and Personality Dynamics". Ronald, New York.

Newcomb, T. M. (1950). "Social Psychology". Dryden, New York.

Newcomb, T. M. (1964). "A Dictionary of the Social Sciences". (Ed. J. Gould and W. L. Kolb) Tavistock, London.

Orme, J. (1971). "An introduction to Abnormal Psychology". Methuen, London.

Peters, R. S. (1958). "The Concept of Motivation". Routledge & Kegan Paul, London.

Philip, A. E. (1973). Assessing punitiveness with the Hostility and Direction of Hostility Questionnaire (HDHQ). *British Journal of Psychiatry*, **123**, 435–439.

Presly, A. S. and Walton, H. J. (1973). Dimensions of abnormal personality. *British Journal of Psychiatry*, **122**, 269–276.

Priest, R. G., Shariatmadari, M. E. and Taraighati, S. (1973). Affective states in schizophrenia. *British Journal of Social and Clinical Psychology*, **22**, 283–288.

Raven, J. C. (1952). "Human Nature". H. K. Lewis, London.

Rogers, C. (1957). The necessary and sufficient conditions of therapeutic personality change. *Journal of Consulting Psychology*, **21**, 95–103.

Rogers, C. (1961). "On Becoming a Person". Constable, London.

Rogers, C. (editor) (1967). "The Therapeutic Relationship and its Impact". University of Wisconsin Press, Madison, Milwaukee and London.

Rosenzweig, S. (1934). Types of reaction to frustration, *Journal of Abnormal and Social Psychology*, **29**, 298–300.

Roth, S. (1970). The seemingly ubiquitous depression following acute schizophrenic episodes: a neglected area of clinical discussion. *American Journal of Psychiatry*, **127**, 51–58.

Rush, Linda, (1970). "Flatness of Affect in Schizophrenia: its Measurement and Relationship to Sub-classifications". Unpublished M.A. dissertation, University of Western Ontario.

Scadding, J. G. (1967). Diagnosis: the clinician and the computer. *Lancet*, **2**, 877–882.

Schneider, K. (1958). "Psychopathic Personalities". Cassell, London.

Shapiro, M. B. (1961). "The Personal Questionnaire. A Method of Measuring Changes in the Symptoms of an Individual Psychiatric Patient". Institute of Psychiatry, London.

Shepherd, M., Brooke, E. M., Cooper, J. E. and Lin, T. (1968). An experimental approach to psychiatric diagnosis. *Acta Psychiatrica Scandinavica, Suppl.* **201**.

Siegel, S. (1956). "Nonparametric Statistics: for the Behavioural Sciences". McGraw-Hill, New York.

Slater, E. and Roth, M. (1969). "Clinical Psychiatry". 3rd edition. Bailliere, Tindall and Cassell, London.

Slater, E. (1975). The Psychiatrist in Search of a Science, III. The Depth Psychologies. *British Journal of Psychiatry*, **126**, 205–224.

Spitzer, R. L. and Endicott, J. (1973). The value of the interview for the evaluation of psychopathology, 397–408. *In* "Psychopathology" (Ed. M. Hammer, K. Salzinger and S. Sutton). Wiley, New York.

Szasz, T. (1960). The Myth of Mental Illness. *American Psychologist*, **15**, 113–118.

Szasz, T. (1971). Review of "A Question of Madness' by Z. A. Medvedev and R. A. Medvedev. Macmillan, London. *In New Society*, 16th December.

Taylor, F. K. (1971). A logical analysis of the medico-psychological concept of disease. *Psychological Medicine*, **1**, 356–364.

Truax, C. B. (1966). Reinforcement and nonreinforcement in Rogerian psychotherapy. *Journal of Abnormal Psychology*. **71**, 1–9.

Walker, Valerie J. (1973). Explanation in obsessional neurosis. *British Journal of Psychiatry*, **123**, 675–680.

Walton, H. J., Foulds, G. A., Littmann, S. K. and Presly, A. S. (1970). Abnormal Personality. *British Journal of Psychiatry*, **116**, 497–510.

Wheelis, A. (1969). The quest for identity. *In* "Behaviour Disorders" (Ed. O. Milton and R. G. Wahler) Lippincott, New York.

Williams, E. and Quirke, C. (1972). Psychological construing in schizophrenics. *British Journal of Medical Psychology*, **45**, 79–84.

Wadsworth, M. E. J., Butterfield, W. J. H. and Blaney, R. (1971). "Health and Sickness: the Choice of Treatment: Tavistock, London.

Wing, J. K. and Brown, G. W. (1970). "Institutionalism and Schizophrenia", Cambridge University Press, Cambridge.

Wing, J. K., Cooper, J. E. and Sartorius, N. (1974). "The Measurement and Classification of Psychiatric Symptoms". Cambridge University Press, London.

Wolpe, J. (1964). Behaviour Therapy in complex neurotic states. *British Journal of Psychiatry*, **110**, 28–34.

Zubin, J. (1967). Classification of the behaviour disorders. *In* "Annual Review of Psychology". Annual Review Inc., Palo Alto.

Index